REVISED AND EXPANDED
GIANT BASIC SKILLS™
3rd GRADE WORKBOOK

W9-AWB-817

Modern Publishing
A Division of Unisystems, Inc.
New York, New York 10022
Series UPC #49115

Cover art by Francesca Rizzo
Illustrated by Arthur Friedman
Educational Consultant, Ellen R. Keller, M.A.

TO THE PARENTS

Dear Parents,

Educators agree that the best guarantee for a child's educational future is a solid grounding in the basics. Parents and caregivers can help by encouraging children every step of the way. With the Revised and Expanded Giant Basic Skills 3rd Grade Workbook, you give them a chance to practice their skills and have fun at the same time. This entertaining but educationally sound workbook will inspire self-starters and reluctant learners alike to enjoy their learning experience with confidence.

This workbook also provides a wonderful opportunity for you and your child to spend quality time together. If your child wants extra support, working on each page together will allow you to reinforce his or her learning. If your child prefers to work independently, you can provide encouragement by reviewing answers and discussing the material. All parents will enjoy the opportunity to think creatively with their children as they read the *How About This* questions posed on many pages.

To help your child get the most out of this book, we suggest that you follow these guidelines:

- Choose a time when your child is relaxed.

- Don't try to do too many pages in a single sitting.

- Make sure your child has pencils, crayons, markers, or other writing tools.

- Encourage your child to browse through the book to find subject matter that catches his or her attention.

- Assure your child that it's okay to ask you questions as he or she works.

- Allow your child to work as independently as he or she feels confident to.

- Follow up by helping your child relate the stories, writing activities, and math problems to everyday experiences.

- Enjoy your time together, and always praise your child's effort.

- Encourage your child to use the practice pages provided at the end of the MATH, MATH MASTER'S PUZZLE BOOK, and CURSIVE WRITING sections to work independently and reinforce skills.

- Use the Achievement Checklist to keep track of which pages you need to revisit. When the "Mastered" column is full, your child has earned the diploma at the back of the book!

Happy learning!

ESSENTIAL SKILLS

Each section of this book starts at a beginner level and gradually progresses to more difficult material. The activities were designed to help children increase their confidence as they develop the skills to face more advanced challenges.

CHAPTER 1 Reading

This section helps children focus on understanding what they read. They learn to **follow directions, classify information,** and **develop analogies.** Identifying **pronoun referents** and **parts of speech** helps new readers understand sentences more precisely. Children are asked to think about short paragraphs and stories, **drawing conclusions** from them, identifying **sequence** and **cause and effect,** and **predicting outcomes.** Children also practice **noticing details, finding the main idea** of a passage, and **using context clues.** They use **sight reading** to recognize many short, common words found in every piece of writing. Finally, they explore **creative writing.**

CHAPTER 2 Math

Every new math skill a child acquires builds upon what was learned before. In this section, children **add numbers up to three digits long, subtract numbers up to three digits long,** and **regroup.** They use **mental math** to think algebraically, practice **skip counting by 2s, 5s,** and **10s** to help understand **odd and even,** and learn to **round and estimate.** Using blocks and **place value charts,** they will come to **understand numbers through the hundred-thousands. Multiplication tables** will help them **multiply and divide one-digit and two-digit numbers** with and without **regrouping.** Children use **greater-than and less-than signs,** and try a variety of **word problems.** They will also explore **fractions, decimals, money, time, graphs,** and **measuring length and volume.**

MATH MASTER'S PUZZLE BOOK

This special section features rewarding puzzles in which children must solve math problems in order to reveal fun pictures.

CHAPTER 3 Language Arts

Understanding the mechanics of grammar helps children grow into stronger readers and writers. This chapter familiarizes children with **common nouns, proper nouns, pronouns, possessive forms of nouns and pronouns,** and **pluralization.** They learn how to use **irregular verbs** and **verbs** in the **past, present, and future tenses.** Understanding **adjectives, adverbs,** and **synonyms** helps them write with **colorful language,** as does using **opposites** and **contractions.** Such practical details as the proper use of **capitalization** and **commas** make children better writers. They will also **identify sentences as complete ideas** with both **subjects** and **predicates,** noting the differences between **statements, questions,** and **exclamations.**

CHAPTER 4 Spelling and Phonics

To expand children's reading and writing vocabulary, there is no better tool than the study of spelling and phonics. In this chapter, **consonant sounds, long vowel sounds,** and **short vowel sounds** are reviewed. **Consonant blends** and **digraphs** are explained. Children will study a wide variety of **irregular pronunciations and spellings,** including **silent letters** such as –**gh** and –**ght.** The spelling rules for **creating plurals** and **creating past-tense verbs** are reviewed in depth.

CHAPTER 5 Cursive Writing

Third grade marks the beginning of children's use of cursive writing. This chapter gives children an opportunity to **write lowercase letters and uppercase letters.** To become more familiar with the cursive alphabet, they **explore small differences between similar letter forms** and practice **writing words and entire sentences** in cursive.

TABLE OF CONTENTS

READING

All About You

Who is one of the most important people? You, of course! Please fill in some important information here.

Draw your street and the place where you live.

Draw a picture of yourself in your favorite clothes.
Add some other favorite things.

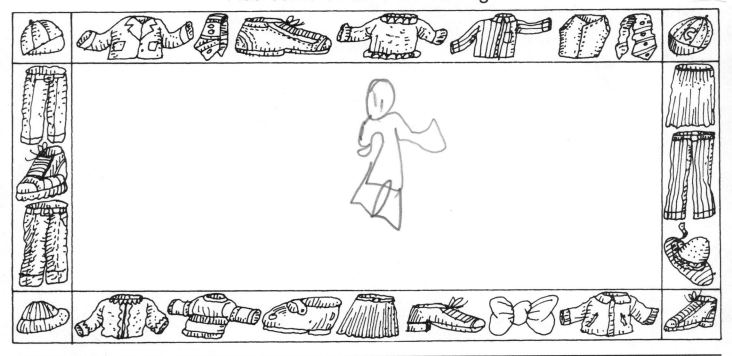

Reading Skill: Following directions

READING

Make a list of your favorite people.

Make a list of your favorite foods.

Make a list of your favorite TV show and movie titles.

Explain why you like making lists or why you hate making lists.

Reading Skill: Following directions

7

READING

Around Town

Lori and Carolyn are walking home from school. Help them get home in time by following the directions. Circle all the stop signs on the way!

- Walk straight out the front door of the school.
- Go forward three blocks.
- Turn right at the corner and walk past the park.
- Turn right at the sliding board.
- Walk 3 blocks.
- Turn right at the corner.
- Go 1 block and turn right.
- Stop at the house with a round window.
- Circle it—that's home!

How about this? *Was this the fastest way for Lori and Carolyn to get home? Do you know the fastest way to get from school to your home? How would you explain this to someone else? Would you draw a map?*

Reading Skill: Following directions

READING

Blast-Off!

It's time to take a little ride. But this is no ordinary car, boat, plane, or train!
Connect the dots from **A** to **Z** to find out how you'll travel.

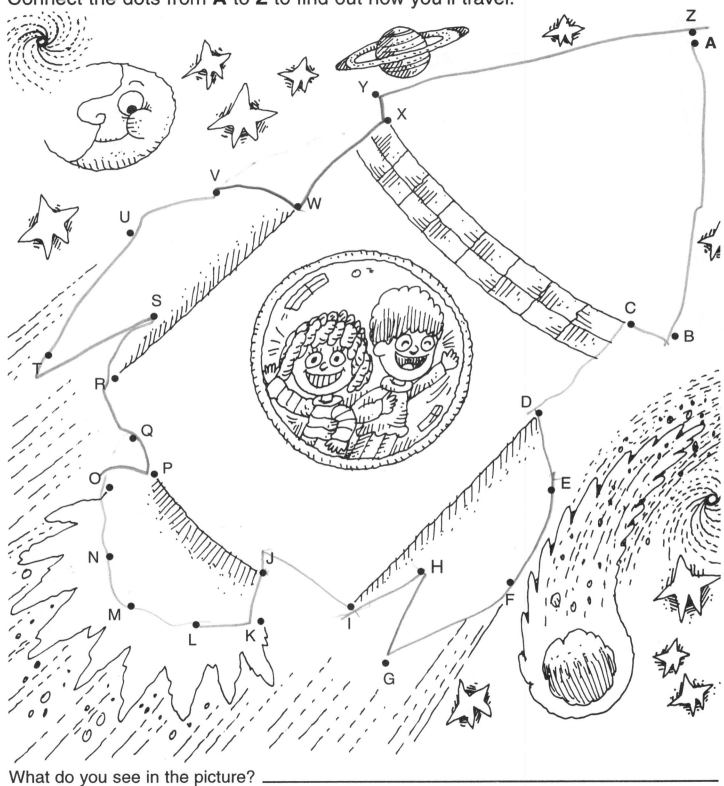

What do you see in the picture? _____

Reading Skill: Reinforcing order of uppercase letters

READING

Outta This World!

Space exploration is moving at a rapid pace. Soon you may need an intergalactic identification card—so fill it out now.

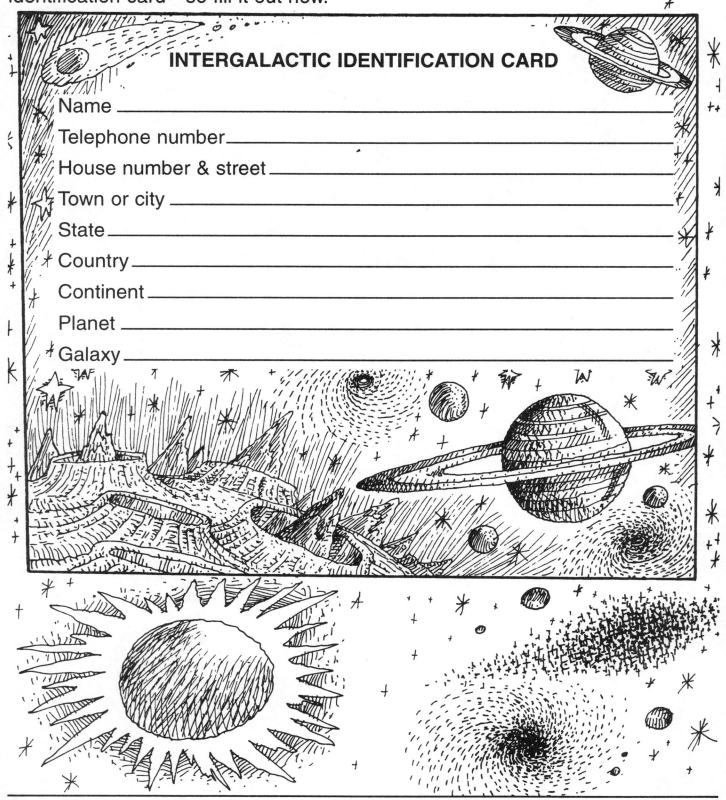

INTERGALACTIC IDENTIFICATION CARD

Name _____

Telephone number _____

House number & street _____

Town or city _____

State _____

Country _____

Continent _____

Planet _____

Galaxy _____

Reading Skill: Following directions

READING

An Intergalactic Survey

The Intergalactic Board wants to know more about you! Please fill out their survey.

Describe a special feature about your physical self.

_____

Describe a special feature about your mind.

_____

What languages do you speak?
Pig Latin counts!

_____

_____

_____

What special talents
do you have?

_____

_____

_____

Please provide the Board
with a picture of yourself
in your space suit.

Reading Skill: Following directions

Five Friends

Read all the clues. Then write a name on every kid's shirt.

- Max is wearing sunglasses.
- Max is between Annie and Lola.
- Tom is next to Lola.
- Stacy is next to Annie.

Reading Skill: Drawing conclusions

READING

Big Talk, Big Words

How can you figure out what a big word means? Use other words nearby to figure it out! Read the following pairs of sentences. Do you know what the **bold** word means? Circle a word or words in the other sentence that means the same thing.

Some people are so crabby.
I don't know what makes them so **cantankerous**.

I like to **collaborate** with my friends on a project.
When we work together, we get a lot done.

I will **ponder** the problem until I find the answer.
All I need to do is think very hard about it.

That mouse in the cartoon is so cowardly.
I have never seen such a **pusillanimous** mouse.

How about this? *Which one of those big words did you like the best? How could you impress people by using this word? How many times a day could you use it? Write a sentence showing how you will use this word.*

Reading Skill: Using context clues

THinking About Little Words

Read the story. Then follow the directions on these two pages.

Max never had trouble reading big words. It was the little words that drove him crazy! So this is what he did. He drew tall boxes around the tall letters and short boxes around the short letters. Then he memorized how the words looked! He ran his finger over each word again and again. Max pictured each word in his mind. Pretty soon, he could remember what those words were when he was reading.

Trace the shapes that Max drew around these **th** words.

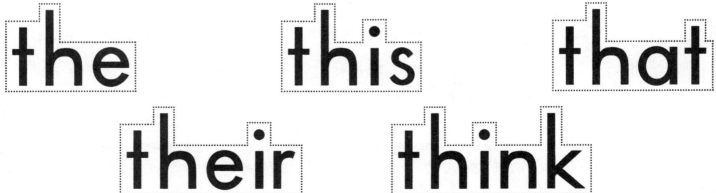

Reading Skill: Sight reading

READING

WHich Little Words?

Question words that started with **wh** gave Max even more trouble. Can you draw lines matching each word with the shape it makes? One is done for you.

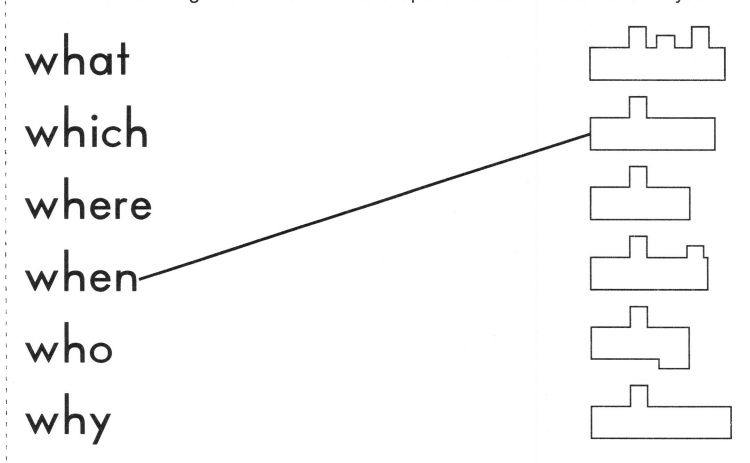

what

which

where

when

who

why

Do you have any words that mix you up? Write them here. Draw boxes around them to help you remember how they look.

How about this? *Think about words you mix up. You could make cards like Max did. They could help you memorize the words.*

Reading Skill: Sight reading

You Must Be Joking

Number each set of sentences in **1, 2, 3** order.

__2__ The man says, "Waiter, what is that fly doing in my soup?"
__3__ The waiter says, "The backstroke."
__1__ A man walks into a restaurant and orders soup.

__3__ "They are both purple," says the girl. "Except for the chicken."
__1__ A girl asks a boy, "How is a chicken like a glass of grape juice?"
__2__ "I don't know," says the boy.

How about this? *Do you know any good jokes? How could you change the jokes you just read to make new ones?*

Reading Skill: Identifying sequence

READING

What Next?
Read the sentence. Then find a picture that shows what will happen next. Write the number of the picture near the sentence.

____ Doofus is walking backward near the lake.
____ Doofus is trying to climb a tree.
____ Doofus is taking a shortcut through the mud.
____ Doofus is standing on his head in his boat.

Reading Skill: Predicting outcomes

READING

Never Bored

Read the story. Then answer the questions.

The Ferd family is never bored. Dad stays in the house and paints the insides of things. He paints the inside of the bathtub once a week. He even paints the insides of his shoes. Mom goes outside and climbs things. Mom climbs flag poles. Mom could climb up the side of your house. The baby makes mud with little piles of sand. She puts it on the sidewalk. She puts it in her crib. She will put it on you if you let her. Freddy Ferd likes to skate, but only indoors. He skates across the tiny bathroom floor. He skates in the elevator. Everyone in the Ferd family has fun.

Who does something outside? _____

Who does something inside? _____

Who does something inside and outside? _____

Which one are you most like? Tell why._____

_____

How about this? *What if you lived with the Ferd family? How weird would you be? Draw yourself in the picture.*

Reading Skill: Recalling details

18

READING

From Top to Bottom

Alex is riding the water slide! Follow the path of lowercase letters from **a** to **z** to help him reach his friends.

Reading Skill: Reinforcing lowercase letter order

Rollin'!
Write a word in each sentence about in-line skating. These rules are the same for pigs or kids.

Put a _____ on your head.

Put kneepads on your _____.

Put _____ on your hands.

knees gloves helmet

Stay away from _____ on sidewalks.

Stay away from _____ kids.

Stay away from all _____.

streets people little

Go slowly before you go _____.

Watch where you are _____.

Stop when you get_____.

tired fast going

Practice new moves in a _____ place.

Wear clothes you can't_____ over.

Take good _____ of your wheels .

care safe trip

Reading Skill: Using context clues

20

READING

All About Things

Read the words in the box. Then write each one in the correct list.

bed
rain
shoes
trouble
pizza
coat
spaghetti
toast
jacket
movies
apples
slime
cap
people's business

Things to Wear

_____
_____
_____
_____

Things to Eat

_____
_____
_____
_____

Things to Get Into

_____
_____
_____
_____

Things to Stay Out Of

_____
_____
_____
_____

How about this? Make your own puzzle! Gather four things and have someone guess what makes them belong to the same group.

Reading Skill: Classifying information

A Bunch of Winners!

Read the story about each kid. Then circle one sentence that tells why that kid is a winner.

It happened every day after school. Tony sat down for twenty minutes and worked on his spelling list. He wrote the words. He said them out loud. He had his sister test him. On Friday, Tony took the spelling test in class. Every week it was the same. He always got a perfect score.

How come?
- Tony could spell from the day he was born.
- The teacher made the test really easy.
- Tony worked hard to learn the words.

Jessica wanted a new bike more than anything. She saved all of her allowance every other week. She saved all the money from gifts. She did jobs for the lady next door. She was paid a quarter, or a dollar, or sometimes five dollars. It took two years. Then Jessica had her new bike.

How come?
- Jessica begged and begged until her dad bought the bike.
- Jessica saved almost all of the money she got.
- The lady next door got the bike for Jessica.

Reading Skill: Identifying cause and effect

Nobody liked the new kid, Tim. No reason—they just didn't like him. Charles was different. He asked Tim to eat a snack with him. He asked about the new kid's old school. Pretty soon Tim began to talk. He was so funny. Then everyone started to like him.

How come?
- Charles made the other kids be nice to the new kid.
- Everyone saw that Charles liked the new kid.
- The new kid was a really good singer.

Maisie knew it wasn't fair. Why should her mom have to do all the cooking and cleaning? Why should her mom have to work so hard at home after working so hard at her job? Maisie got her older brother to do some cooking. She got her younger sister to straighten up the house. Maisie spent one hour every day after school doing whatever needed to be done. Soon Maisie's mother wasn't so tired any more.

How come?
- Maisie and her brother started ordering pizza for dinner.
- Maisie and her brother and sister helped out.
- Maisie's mother went on a vacation to the Caribbean.

How about this? Think about something new you could do to be a winner. Talk to someone about it. Then do it!

Reading Skill: Identifying cause and effect

READING

Dressing Up

Everyone is planning for the backyard show. Read about the costumes they are making. What do you think they will be? Write the answers.

Patty and Tim find big hats. They put on tall boots. Each one is carrying a long rope. "Howdy, pardner," Patty calls out to Tim. Tim is singing a song called "Home, Home on the Range." What will Patty and Tim be in the show? How do you know?

_____

_____

_____

Ashley cuts a whole pile of newspapers into strips. Then she pastes all the strips to a ribbon. She ties the ribbon around her waist. The strips hang from her waist to her knees. Then Ashley makes a necklace of paper flowers. She makes two small ones for her wrists. Then Ashley practices her dance. What kind of dancer will she be? How do you know?

_____

_____

_____

How about this? *What kind of costume could you make? Look through books for an idea. Make the costume in your own special way.*

Reading Skill: Drawing conclusions

READING

Odd or Awesome?
Circle the word or words nearby that mean the same thing as the bold word.

Nork from Gork thought the Planet Earth was the most **awesome** place.
To Nork, Earth was unbelievable and wonderful.

But Nork thought some things about Earth were **bizarre**.
He said it was strange that people moved on things called "feet."

Instead of walking, Nork liked to **levitate**.
Nork floated in the air over everyone's head.

Flying among the Earth people made Nork feel **invincible**.
When Nork played tag with the Earth kids, he would always win.

One day Nork played tag with a girl who could jump to an amazing height.
She finally tagged Nork by jumping to the **altitude** where he was flying!

Reading Skill: Using context clues

READING

Fill 'er Up

Rewrite each set of words in alphabetical order.

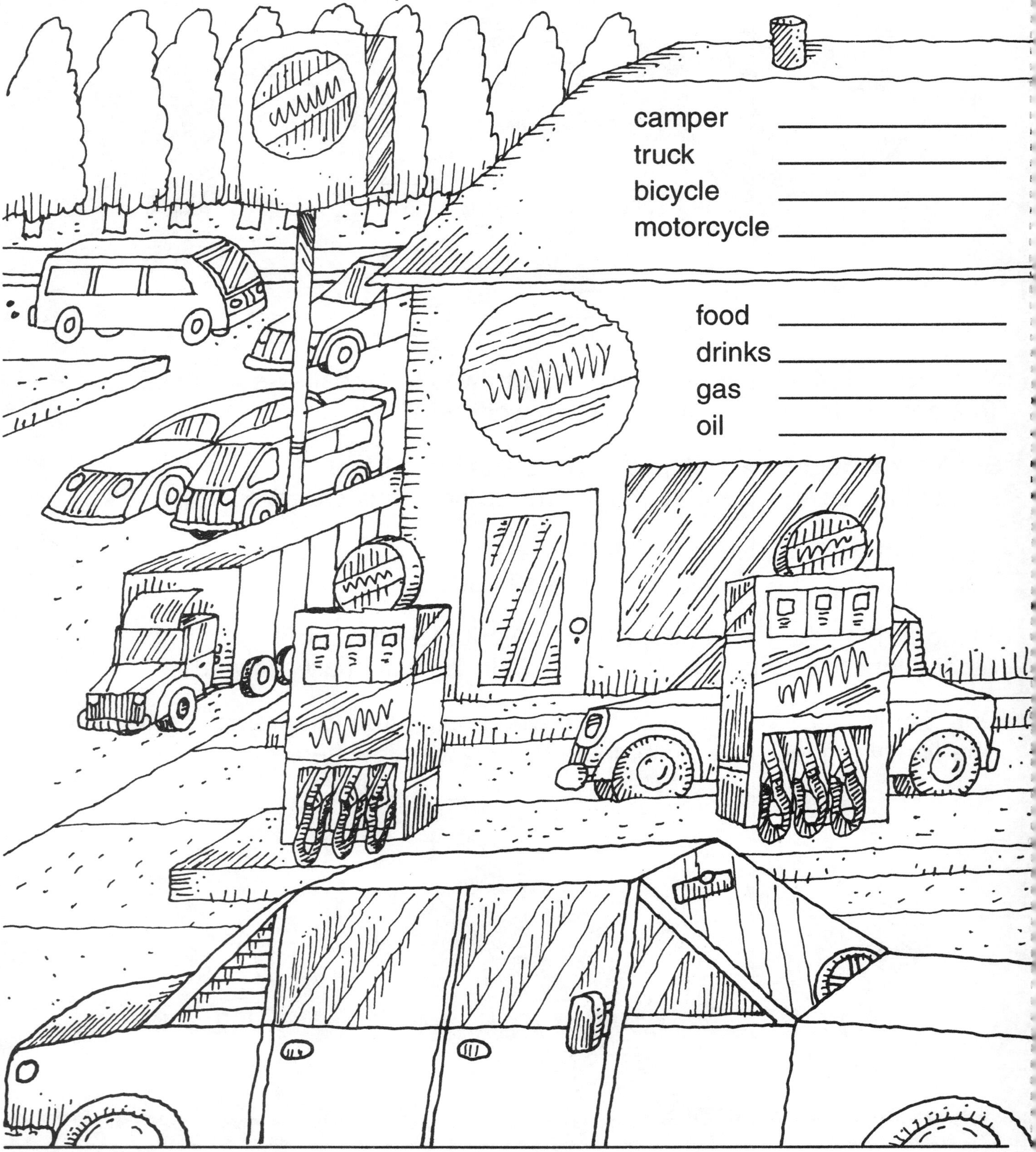

camper   _____

truck   _____

bicycle   _____

motorcycle _____

food   _____

drinks   _____

gas   _____

oil   _____

Reading Skill: Placing words in alphabetical order

READING

driver _____
passenger _____
tires _____
motor _____

candy _____
cookies _____
caramels _____
soda

treats _____
trailer _____
tracks _____
traffic _____

Reading Skill: Placing words in alphabetical order

READING

The Disappearing Can

Here's a magic trick for you to try. To find out how to do it, number the first set of sentences **1** through **5**. Number the second set of sentences **6** through **10**.

_____ After you find the can and a newspaper, sit down at a table.

_____ Slide the wrapped can across the table toward your friend. Have him feel the can inside the paper.

_____ Get an empty soda can and a newspaper.

_____ When everything is ready, ask your friend to sit across from you at the table.

_____ Wrap the newspaper tightly around the top and sides of the can.

_____ Say "Tah-dah!" and wait for the applause!

_____ If you feel like it, show your friend how you did this disappearing can trick.

_____ Say "abra-cadabra," "ka-chung ka-chang," or any other magic stuff. Then smash your fist down on the empty newspaper shape.

_____ Slide the can back toward you, off the edge of the table.

_____ Let the can fall into your lap, but keep holding the newspaper in the can shape.

Reading Skill: Identifying sequence

READING

The Same and Different

Homonyms are words that sound alike but have different meanings. Circle a word that goes with each picture. Then write some of the words in sentences below.

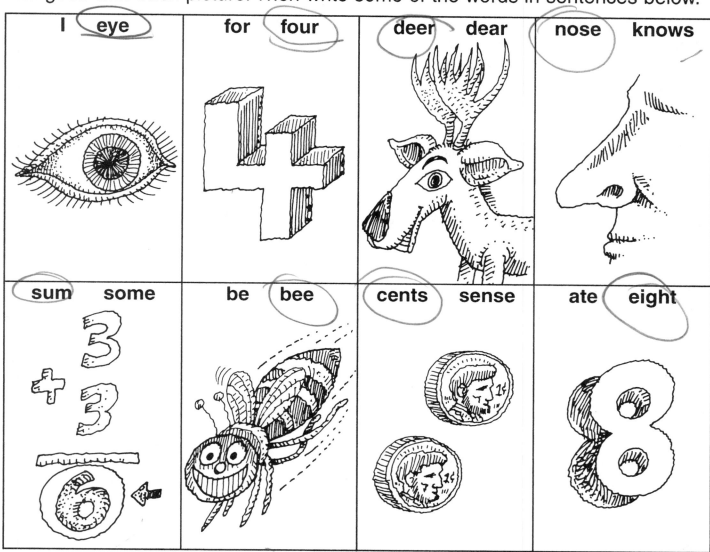

I (eye)   for (four)   (deer) dear   (nose) knows

sum some   be (bee)   (cents) sense   ate (eight)

Kelly and __I__ went to the mall.

We __ate__ pizza and drank juice for lunch.

I got a poster with a buzzing __be__ on it.

The clerk gave me one dollar change from five dollars because the
    poster cost __four__ dollars.

I also got __some__ stickers and a box of crayons.

Reading Skill: Understanding the meaning of homonyms

Believe It or Not

Read these two stories. Then circle the words that make the best title.

Some things are strange. Some things are hard to believe. The mystery of the old Hayden house in Maryland is very strange indeed. The house was built in the 1800s and many families lived there through the years. Part of the house is still standing. New parts have been added to make offices and a library.

No one knows when the strange things started happening. Lights began to turn off and on in the office rooms. The electric coffee pot heated up. It wasn't plugged in. A rocking chair would move back and forth. No one was sitting in it. At least there was no one that anyone could see.

People working overtime, late at night, were terrified. They would hear a noise behind them. A door would swing open and closed. Smells of cooking filled the rooms: coffee, soup, bacon, and eggs. Workers began to call it "the cooking ghost." But make no mistake, this was no laughing matter.

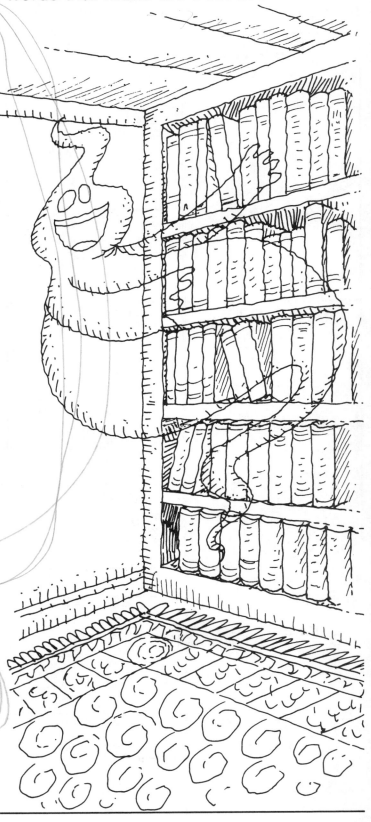

- Great Fun in Maryland
- Terror in the Old House
- Cooking Breakfast
- The Swinging Rocking Chair

Reading Skill: Finding the main idea

Believe it or not, some people think there are ghosts everywhere. What are ghosts? They are supposed to be people who died before their time. They might also be people who died in some terrible way. This is odd, because people who say they have seen ghosts also say that the ghosts never seemed angry. They do not mean any harm. Ghosts never hurt people. Okay, some make strange noises. People get scared. But most of the time, ghosts are said to ignore people in a haunted house. Or ghosts may act gently and kindly.

You wouldn't believe some of the things people think about ghosts. Here's one thing. If you were born at night, you will never see a ghost. Here's another thing. Ghosts are supposed to be afraid of other ghosts. If they see themselves in a mirror, they run away. Also, ghosts are supposed to be afraid of water. They will never cross a river or a lake.

Actually, there probably aren't any ghosts. But they are fun to think about!

- Ghosts and Where They Come From
- A Ghost Looks in the Mirror
- Ghostly Walks on Water
- Facts and Fantasies About Ghosts

Reading Skill: Finding the main idea

READING

The Rise of Surtsey
Read each paragraph. Then number the sentences in order.

The month was November. The year was 1963. The place was a spot in the ocean 70 miles away from Iceland. All week long, the crew of a nearby ship had been smelling a strange chemical odor in the air. Then, on the morning of November 14, it happened! There were shaky rumblings. It was as though there were an earthquake. Smoke and fire appeared to float on top of the water. Then all at once a new island burst up from beneath the sea.

____ Fire and smoke appeared to float on the water.
____ A new island burst up from the sea.
____ People smelled a strange odor in the air.
____ The earth shook as if there were an earthquake.

The news spread throughout the world. A new island was born. It was the island they would later call Surtsey. In six days a volcano on the island grew to 230 feet. Explosions of fire and melted rock (called "magma") flew up. Five months later, the island had grown to the size of a half mile. One month later, some of the volcano lava had cooled to form cliffs. Birds came. In June of 1965, the first growing plant was found.

____ Cliffs were formed.
____ The island was a half mile wide.
____ The first plant grew on the island.
____ The volcano grew to over 200 feet.

How about this? *Where could you find out more about Surtsey? Who could help you find some information?*

Reading Skill: Identifying sequence

READING

Good Books

Words in a sentence give you clues about what a missing word should be. Read each sentence for clues. Then write a word from the list on each line.

I like to read scary books in the daytime but not at _____.

Joke books always make me _____.

The first book I learned to _____ had funny pictures.

The hero in a detective story solves a _____.

Ted is the main _____ in the book I'm reading.

When I am tired, I like to read a book that is _____ to read.

| easy | read | laugh | mystery | night | character |

Once I _____ my own book about Halloween.

Sometimes, I take turns reading stories out loud with my _____.

If a book is really good, I read it more than _____.

I save my _____ so I can buy a book or a magazine.

At a secondhand bookstore, I can buy a book for two _____.

I like a story that has a happy _____.

| friends | once | wrote | ending | money | dollars |

How about this? *Find a book that looks good to you. Read just a few pages at the beginning to see if the characters are anything like you. You might want to read more.*

Reading Skill: Using context clues

READING

Wolves
Read the story. Then answer the questions.

Deep in the north woods, you may hear howling on a cold winter night. It sounds scary. But it is only the wolves calling out to each other. Wolves live together in packs of about ten. One wolf is the leader. When wolves hunt for food, they spread out. One wolf who finds food calls out to the others to come.

Young wolves have many babysitters. Old male and female wolves are in charge of the babies when the parents go out looking for food. Wolves of all ages enjoy playing with others in the pack. Rolling around on the ground and wrestling is a favorite game.

You would never want to get too close to a wild wolf. However, stories of wolves attacking people are probably not true. Wolves usually want to stay as far away from people as they can.

How many wolves might live in one pack?

_____

Why do wolves howl?

_____

How do wolves play?

_____

What do babysitters have to do with wolves?

_____

What might a wolf do if it saw a person? What makes you say that?

_____

_____

_____

Reading Skill: Recalling details

READING

What Will Happen?

Read the paragraph. Then circle the sentence that tells what will happen.

Meg drinks the rest of her orange juice. She puts the dishes in the sink. Then Meg goes into the bathroom. She brushes her teeth. Meg finds her backpack. She puts her homework in it. Meg puts on her jacket. Then she goes out the door.

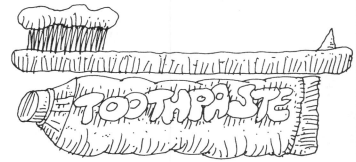

- Meg will go to the mall.
- Meg will go to school.
- Meg will go to the movies.

Jenny and Justin drag a big box into the backyard. They put it next to the fence. Then they put a blanket over the fence. They pull out one side of the blanket to make a tent. Jenny crawls through the box and into the blanket tent. "We can fit three kids in here at one time," she says. "That is you and me and one other kid."

- Jenny will take a nap on the blanket.
- Jenny and Justin will invite another kid into their tent.
- Jenny and Justin will invite another kid to go to the movies.

Reading Skill: Predicting outcomes

READING

What Goes Together?

Read each group of words. Why do they belong together? Add another word from the list that fits in the group.

| cup | cat | beans | bottle | sheet | water | door | crayons | jacket |

gerbil
dog
goldfish

_____

socks
shoes
cap

_____

pencils
paper
paints

_____

plate
fork
spoon

_____

carrots
lettuce
cucumbers

_____

juice
milk
soda

_____

Reading Skill: Classifying information

Same Sounds, Different Spelling

Homonyms are all around you! Look at each sentence below. Read the **bold** word. Circle another word in the sentence that sounds the same but has a different spelling and meaning.

I have a hole in my pants, so I will learn to **sew**.

All I **ate** today was eight tiny beans.

The **bare** little baby ran outside holding a teddy bear.

I got four apples **for** one dollar.

She knows her **nose** hurts when she has a cold.

It doesn't make any **sense** to sell a hot dog for two cents.

The book I **read** had a red cover.

I do **not** have a knot in my shoelace.

I will go **to** the show with two friends.

I want to **write** your name in the right way.

How about this? *Choose one pair of words from the sentences. Use those words in a sentence or two of your own. Then draw a picture of what you wrote.*

Reading Skill: Identifying homonyms

READING

Mix and Match

Look at the picture in each box. Can you match the pictures that belong together? Draw lines to connect them.

How about this? *Look at each box again. Can you explain why you made those matches? What do the matches have in common?*

Reading Skill: Finding analogies

READING

What Are They?
Write a word from the list to complete each sentence.

clothing	colors	girls	boys	feelings
pets	vegetables	fun	fruits	read

Wendy, Nicole, and Joanna are all names of _____.

Kevin, David, and Anthony are all names of _____.

Red, green, and blue are all _____.

Happy, sad, and excited are words that describe our _____.

Apples, oranges, and grapes are names of _____.

Shirt, jeans, and caps are _____.

Carrots, beans, and peas are _____.

Kickball, soccer, and ping-pong are _____.

Books, magazines, and newspapers are things we can _____.

Reading Skill: Classifying information

READING

Extra! Extra! Read All About It!
Look at this front-page story. Everything is out of order! Can you help get the facts straight? Number the sentences from **1** to **4**.

_1_ A girl known as Goldilocks entered the Bear residence when no one was home.

_3_ Next she broke a small chair.

_2_ First she went into the kitchen and ate all the porridge.

_4_ When the Bear family came home, they decided not to press charges.

Reading Skill: Identifying sequence

READING

It's News to Me!

"We interrupt your program for a very important report. The prince needs help!" says the newswoman. But the story is all out of order. Number the sentences from **1** to **4** to figure out what happened.

_____ This morning the prince began looking for the girl.

_____ The prince held a ball last night. He danced with an unknown girl.

_____ At midnight, the girl ran away from the ball, but dropped her shoe.

_____ So far, this evening, she has not been found.

"Anyone who knows the name of the prince's dance partner should call right away!" says the newswoman. If you know the answer, write it here:

_____

How about this? *What is your favorite fairy tale or folk tale? Make up a news broadcast about it. Perform your broadcast for your family, your dog, or the mirror.*

Reading Skill: Identifying sequence

READING

In the Neighborhood

Read each set of sentences. The **bold** word is called a **pronoun**. Write the answer to the question to tell what the pronoun means.

Lauren jumps rope in front of her house. **She** likes to jump rope more than anything.

Who is **She**? _____

Kenny sits on the stairs outside his apartment building. **He** is drawing a picture on paper.

Who is **He**? _____

You and I are eating ice cream. **We** really are enjoying the sweet, creamy treat.

Who are **We**? _____

Reading Skill: Identifying pronoun referents

READING

A Busy Afternoon

There is a lot going on today! Write the answers to the questions to tell what the **bold** pronouns mean.

Kenny sees a big moving van parked outside his apartment building. **He** thinks **it** is filled with furniture and rugs.

Who is **He**? _____

What is **it**? _____

Mrs. Grundy likes to put candles in **her** window. Everyone says **they** are pretty.

Who is **her**? _____

What is **they**? _____

Many of the parents in the neighborhood like to grow flowers in window boxes. Almost every evening, **they** water **them**.

Who is **they**? _____

What is **them**? _____

Reading Skill: Identifying pronoun referents

READING

Making Stuff

Read the stories on these two pages. Then number the sentences from **1** to **5**.

Danny likes to make stuff. One day he collects paper clips, his sister's hair barrettes, and safety pins. Then he calls his little sister. He tells her that they will make some jewelry for her. It will be made from the things he has collected.

First, Danny reminds his five-year-old sister that she shouldn't put any of these things in her mouth. His little sister shouts, "I know that. I'm not a baby." So Danny and his sister hook four paper clips together. Then they hook on a hair barrette. Then they hook on four more paper clips. They keep doing this until they have a necklace. Danny's sister puts on the necklace. "Look at me!" she shouts. "I'm so pretty!" Then Danny makes a safety pin bracelet.

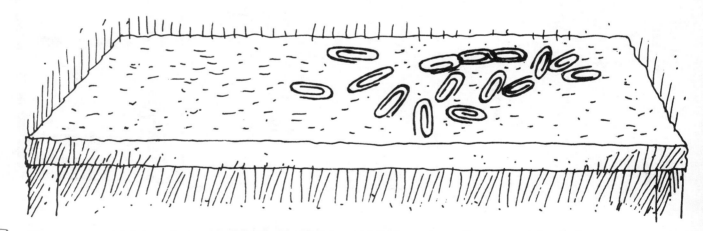

__3__ Danny and his sister make a necklace of paper clips and hair barrettes.

__4__ Danny's sister tries on the necklace.

__1__ Danny collects paper clips, hair barrettes, and safety pins.

__2__ Danny reminds his sister not to put things in her mouth.

__5__ Danny makes a safety pin bracelet.

Reading Skill: Identifying sequence

READING

Mindy and Kate are making play-dough people in Mindy's kitchen. Mindy pours two cups of flour into a bowl. Kate puts in one cup of salt. Then Kate gets a cup of water from the faucet. She pours a little at a time into the bowl. Mindy stirs the mixture. The clay begins to stick together. Then Kate and Mindy make little people. They put the little people on waxed paper. In two hours the little people are hard and dry. Now Kate and Mindy can paint them!

__4__ Mindy stirs the mixture.
__2__ Kate puts in one cup of salt.
__1__ Mindy puts two cups of flour into the bowl.
__5__ In two hours, the little clay people are hard and dry.
__3__ Mindy and Kate make little clay people.

How about this? *What could you make if you put together homemade clay and paper clips? How else could you decorate your clay sculptures? Give it a try.*

Reading Skill: Identifying sequence

READING

More Than One Meaning

Some words have more than one meaning. Write a word from the list that fits both sentences. Do the same thing on the next page, too!

even   rest   can   band

Ben keeps his crayons in a big tin _____.

He _____ spend all day drawing.

Patty likes to _____ after she runs a hard race.

Later, she spends the _____ of the evening doing quiet things.

Nell wears a _____ to hold back her hair.

Next year Nell will play in the _____.

Stacy breaks the cookie in two pieces that are nearly _____.

Stacy doesn't _____ care if she gets the smaller piece.

Reading Skill: Identifying multiple meanings

READING

bark   mean   bank   bear

Toby and Jen sit on the river _____ and talk.

Jen tells Toby that she takes her money to a _____ to save it.

There are some dogs that don't even _____.

The trunk of a tree has _____ on it.

One animal that can be huge, furry, and black is the _____.

They can't _____ to look at scary animals in the movies.

People can't understand what you _____ if you mumble.

Cassie has no friends because she is so _____ to everyone.

Reading Skill: Identifying multiple meanings

49

READING

The Best Back Yard
What if you could have any kind of backyard you wanted? Follow these directions to draw a really good back yard.

Draw these:
- you doing your favorite fun thing
- a swing hanging from the tree
- a sandbox with toys in it
- a pet drinking from a bowl of water
- someone having a picnic or playing a game
- red and purple flowers next to the fence

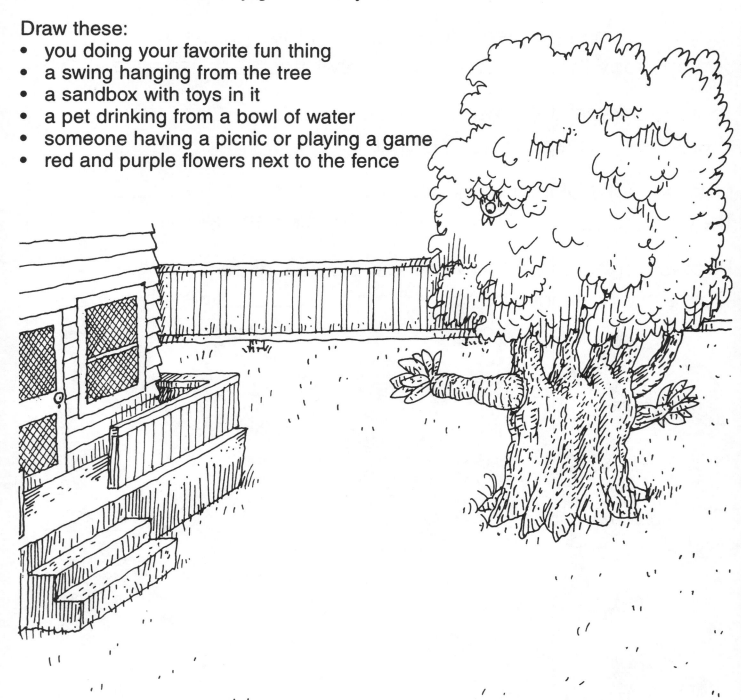

How about this? You could design a back yard in a cardboard box. You can use paper, glue, crayons, and paints. You can make stand-up trees and people from cardboard and clay.

Reading Skill: Following directions

READING

Vampire Knee-Slappers

Read these jokes. Then answer the questions.

A. **Kid**: Mom, tell me something. Am I a vampire?
   Mom: Of course not, dear. And don't forget to make your coffin before you go to school.

B. **Kid**: Dad, why does everyone run away from a vampire?
   Dad: Because he has bat breath.

C. **Kid**: Why did the vampire climb the stairs in the Empire State Building?
   Brother: To get to the top.

D. **Kid**: How does a vampire drive his car over water?
   Sister: He uses a bridge.

What is the same about A, B, C, and D?

_____

_____

_____

_____

Can you make up your own joke?
Make it like those on this page.

_____

_____

_____

_____

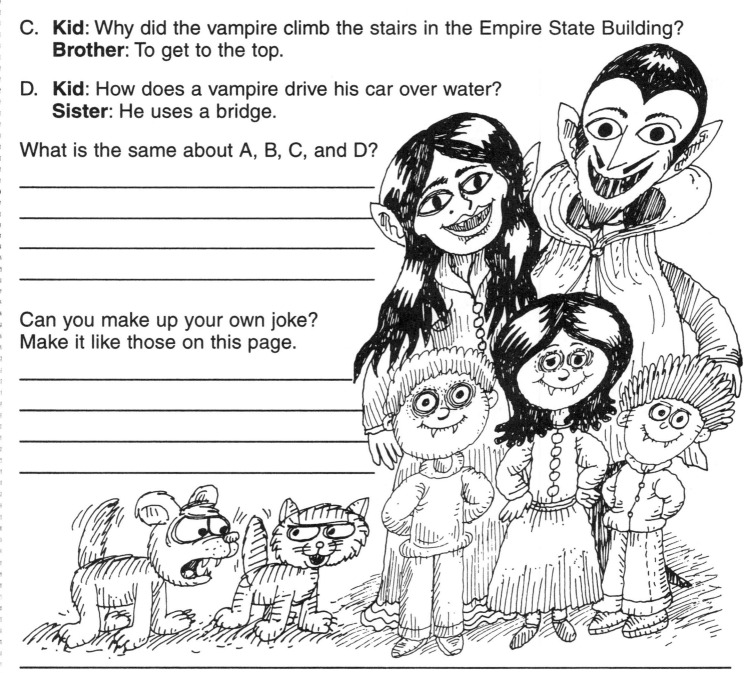

Reading Skill: Finding the main idea

A True Story
Read the story and answer the questions on these two pages.

You have probably heard of Pocahontas. Many stories have been written about her. Some stories are true. Many are not. She was the friend of Captain John Smith and the other men and boys that began the colony of Jamestown about 400 years ago.

Pocahontas was the daughter of the great Indian chief Powhatan. It was said that Powhatan had over 100 children. Whether that was true or not, we do know one thing. Pocahontas was his favorite child. She was only twelve years old when Jamestown began. But her father chose her to be a messenger between himself and the Jamestown leaders. The leaders could see that Pocahontas was smart. She learned many English words and ways. She helped the Jamestown people to survive in their new and strange land.

Circle the title that best tells what the whole story is about.
- The Making of Jamestown
- The True Story of Pocahontas
- Pocahontas Learns English
- Powhatan's 100 Children

Reading Skill: Finding the main idea

READING

Who Can It Be?

This drawing isn't very exciting. Follow the directions to make a picture that is more fun. Then color it in!

- Draw ten straight lines up from the top of his head.
- Trace a penny to make a circle around each eye.
- Draw a rectangle around each circle.
- Draw a half circle on the right side of his head to make an ear.
- Draw a half circle on the left side of his head to make an ear.
- Draw a short eyebrow line over each eye. Don't let the lines touch the eyes!
- Make a line stretching all the way across his open mouth, from corner to corner.
- Draw an up-and-down line right in the middle of his mouth.
- Draw two more up-and-down lines on the left.
- Draw two more up-and-down lines on the right.
- Give this fellow a name! Write it on the space below his chin.

Name: _____

How about this? *Make up your own instructions for drawing a funny face. Have two or three different people draw the face while you read the instructions. Then compare what everybody drew!*

Reading Skill: Following directions

READING

A Bad Day

Tinker's bad day started off bad right away. To find out what happened, number the sentences on these two pages.

Number these sentences **1, 2, 3, 4**:

_____ Tinker looked for a shirt and fell in the closet.

_____ Tinker stepped out of bed and into a bowl of melted ice cream.

_____ Tinker's dog woke him up with loud barking.

_____ Tinker made ice cream tracks on the floor.

Number these sentences **5, 6, 7, 8**:

_____ Tinker left his room in a mess.

_____ Tinker got dressed before he put on his shoes and socks.

_____ Tinker put on his shoes over the sticky ice cream socks.

_____ Tinker got sticky ice cream inside his socks.

Reading Skill: Identifying sequence

READING

Number these sentences **9, 10, 11, 12**:

_____ Tinker went into the kitchen.

_____ Danny sat down and said, "I smell ice cream feet."

_____ Tinker's friend Danny knocked on the kitchen door.

_____ Tinker told Danny to come in and have breakfast.

Number these sentences **13, 14, 15, 16**:

_____ Tinker's teacher said, "Why do I smell ice cream?"

_____ Tinker and Danny walked to school.

_____ Tinker ran home after school because dogs were trying to lick his feet.

_____ That night Tinker told his mom he is never eating ice cream again.

Reading Skill: Identifying sequence

READING

A Good Use for Hot Air

What do you know about physics? A lot more than you think! Every time something moves, it is using physics. Read and think about why things happen. Then answer the questions.

Meg and Jo-Jo are having a race. Each of them takes a sheet of paper and crumples it into a ball. Then they stand at one end of a very long, shiny table. They put the paper balls down on it. At the count of three, they blow hard. They send the balls down the table. The race will be close!

What makes the paper balls go across the table?

What will Meg or Jo-Jo have to do in order to win the race?

The next day, Jo-Jo and Meg have another race. They stand in a lake and use milk cartons for boats. Like before, they blow to make the boats move. But this race is much harder.

Why do you think this race is harder?

How about this? *What kind of race could you invent? It could be anything. You just have to use your own hot air.*

Reading Skill: Identifying cause and effect

READING

A Cool Sea Breeze

The air doesn't have to be hot to move things around! Do you want to see something that uses the wind to help it move? Use the code to fill in this picture:

Color sections with one vowel light blue.
Color sections with one consonant dark blue.
Color sections with a pronoun red.
Color sections with two consonants yellow.

Write the name of what the picture shows here: _____

Reading Skill: Following directions

READING

So Many Books, So Little Time

Read this story about a day at the library. Answer the questions below. Then use what you remember to solve the crossword puzzle on the next page.

Ben's class is at the library. "Don't pick out more books than you can carry home, kids!" says the librarian. Ben picks up a book called "How to Build the Perfect Fort." He picks up another book called "How to Paint Horses." On a low shelf, he chooses a book about famous skateboarders. On a high shelf, he chooses a book about a mouse who is very good at math.

Ben finds ten other books that he wants to read. But there are so many more books. How is Ben going to carry them all home?

Then Ben looks out the window. What is that he sees in the school garden? Ben carries his books over to the librarian. "Please watch these, Miss Stella," he says. Then he runs out the door!

The librarian calls out, "Ben, where are you going?" Everyone in the class looks out the window. And there in the garden is Ben. What is he doing? He is getting the gardener's wheelbarrow!

Proudly, Ben rolls the wheelbarrow into the library. "There!" he says, smiling. "Now I can carry all my books home!"

What is the name of your favorite book?

_____

What subjects do you like to read about?

_____

How would you describe your school library?

_____

_____

Reading Skill: Reading comprehension

READING

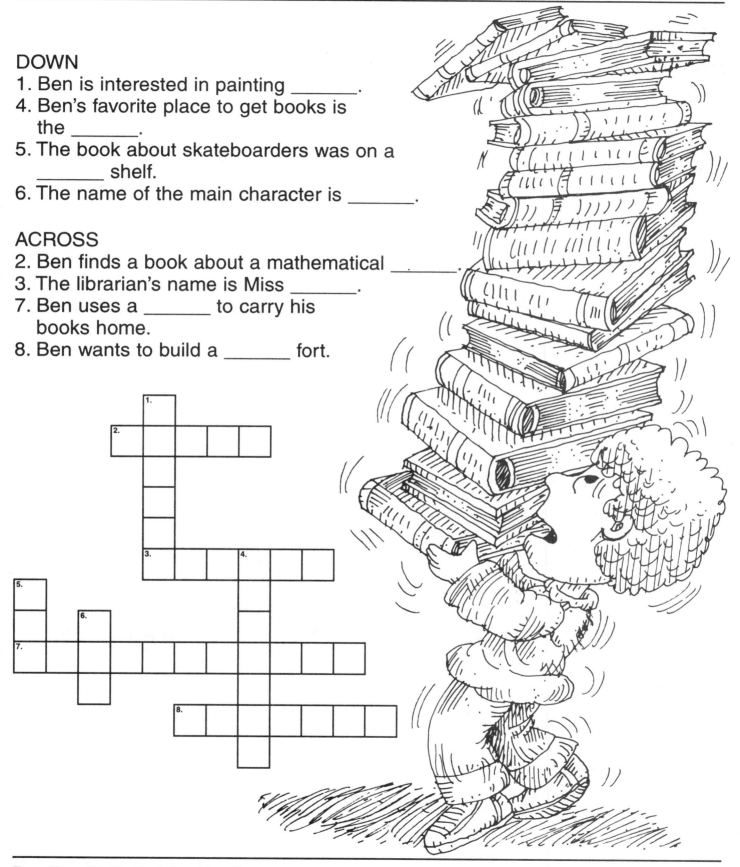

DOWN
1. Ben is interested in painting _____.
4. Ben's favorite place to get books is the _____.
5. The book about skateboarders was on a _____ shelf.
6. The name of the main character is _____.

ACROSS
2. Ben finds a book about a mathematical _____.
3. The librarian's name is Miss _____.
7. Ben uses a _____ to carry his books home.
8. Ben wants to build a _____ fort.

Reading Skill: Noticing details

Double Talk

Doubles are number facts like 2 + 2. Knowing your doubles can help you solve problems quickly. They even help with problems that are not quite doubles, like 2 + 3 and 10 − 5. Try the problems below to see what doubles can do!

2	3	4	5	6	7	8	9
+2	+3	+4	+5	+6	+7	+8	+9

6 + 6 = ___   6 + 7 = ___   7 + 7 = ___   7 + 8 = ___

8 + 8 = ___   8 + 9 = ___   9 + 9 = ___   9 + 10 = ___

12 − 6 = ___   14 − 7 = ___   16 − 8 = ___   18 − 9 = ___

Math Skill: Using doubles to recall addition and subtraction facts

MATH

A Secret Message

Find an answer for each number fact. Then locate that number in the code.
What letter does it stand for? Write it below the problem to decode the message.

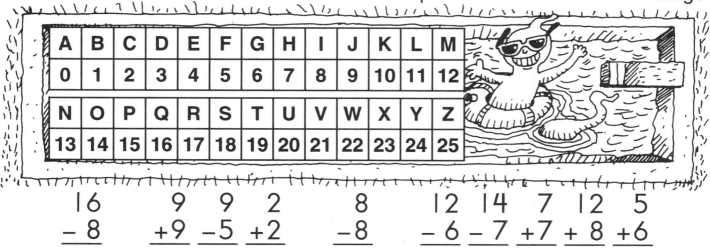

A	B	C	D	E	F	G	H	I	J	K	L	M
0	1	2	3	4	5	6	7	8	9	10	11	12

N	O	P	Q	R	S	T	U	V	W	X	Y	Z
13	14	15	16	17	18	19	20	21	22	23	24	25

```
  16      9   9   2       8     12  14   7  12   5
 - 8     +9  -5  +2      -8    - 6 - 7  +7  + 8 +6

_____  ___ ___ ___    ___    ___ ___ ___ ___ ___


         15   6      10  15  10      7   9   6   4
        - 7  +7     +9  - 8 - 6     +8  +5  +8  +7

        ___ ___    ___ ___ ___    ___ ___ ___ ___
```

How about this? You and a family member could make a secret message book.
Write your secret messages as number facts, and use the code to figure them out!

Math Skill: Reviewing addition and subtraction facts

MATH

Adding More than Two Numbers

Can you add three numbers together? Sure you can! What's great is that you can add them in any order. Look at this—three ways to solve **4 + 5 + 2**!

(4 + 5) = **9**. Then **9** + 2 = 11.
(5 + 2) = **7**. Then **7** + 4 = 11.
(4 + 2) = **6**. Then **6** + 5 = 11.

(1 + 3) + 4 = ____

1 + (3 + 4) = ____

2 + (3 + 3) = ____

(3 + 4) + 5 = ____

2 + 5 + 3 = ____

7 + 3 + 1 = ____

4 + 0 + 6 = ____

2 + 3 + 6 = ____

Claighorne fell in a hole 7 times in the morning. He fell in the washing machine 3 times in the afternoon. Then he fell in the dog dish 6 times at night. What is the matter with Claighorne, anyway? How many times did he fall all together?

_____

How about this? *You and a friend do some mental math. Mental math means there's no writing, only thinking in your head. Your friend names a number like 5. Double it. Then add 1. Then give the answer as fast as you can!*

Math Skill: Using the associative property with addition

MATH

What's Missing?
Find the missing number. Watch the signs!

$7 + 3 = \underline{\qquad}$ $5 - 2 = \underline{\qquad}$ $12 - 9 = \underline{\qquad}$

$4 + \underline{\qquad} = 11$ $9 - \underline{\qquad} = 5$ $15 - 8 = \underline{\qquad}$

$6 + 3 = \underline{\qquad}$ $\underline{\qquad} - 7 = 3$ $\underline{\qquad} - 9 = 9$

$\underline{\qquad} + 3 = 8$ $\underline{\qquad} - 5 = 3$ $\underline{\qquad} - 9 = 8$

The + or − sign is missing. Put it in the circle.

$6 \bigcirc 1 = 5$

$9 \bigcirc 3 = 12$

$7 \bigcirc 3 = 10$

$4 \bigcirc 9 = 13$

$13 \bigcirc 9 = 4$

How about this? *Here's a mental math puzzle! Count all your toes. Add the number of fingers on one hand. Then add the number of eyes you have. How many things is that all together? Ask someone to give you another mental math problem.*

Math Skill: Using mental math to find the sum or the difference

Fact Families

A fact family is a set of related addition and subtraction sentences. All of the number sentences contain the same numbers. Here is a fact family for **3**, **5**, and **8**.

3 + 5 = 8   5 + 3 = 8   8 – 3 = 5   8 – 5 = 3

Add or subtract to complete the fact families.

4 + 5 = ____	3 + 2 = ____	6 + 4 = ____
5 + 4 = ____	2 + 3 = ____	4 + 6 = ____
9 – 5 = ____	5 – 2 = ____	10 – 4 = ____
9 – 4 = ____	5 – 3 = ____	10 – 6 = ____

Add or subtract. Then write one more fact to complete the family.

4 + 3 = ____	6 + 9 = ____	9 + 8 = ____
3 + 4 = ____	9 + 6 = ____	8 + 9 = ____
7 – 3 = ____	15 – 6 = ____	17 – 9 = ____
_____	_____	_____

Write a fact family using **2**, **8**, and **10**.

_____   _____

_____   _____

Math Skill: Recognizing how addition and subtraction interact

MATH

Quick Thinking!
As quick as you can, write numbers on the lines.

Write the number that is 1 less than:

6 ____   13 ____   9 ____   7 ____   1 ____

Write the number that is 2 more than:

3 ____   8 ____   5 ____   4 ____   10 ____

Double the number and add 2:

2 ____   7 ____   3 ____   8 ____   9 ____

How about this? *Play a quick-thinking math game with a friend. Make up a math rule like "add 3." Your friend shouts out a number and you shout out the answer. Then you shout out the number and your friend shouts out the answer! How fast can you get?*

Math Skill: Practicing strategies in mental math

MATH

Even I Think That's Odd

Even numbers can be sorted into pairs. **2**, **4**, and **6** are even numbers. Odd numbers can be sorted into pairs with 1 left over. **3**, **5**, and **7** are odd numbers.

1	2	3	4	5	6	7	8	9	10
11	12	13	14	15	16	17	18	19	20
21	22	23	24	25	26	27	28	29	30
31	32	33	34	35	36	37	38	39	40
41	42	43	44	45	46	47	48	49	50
51	52	53	54	55	56	57	58	59	60
61	62	63	64	65	66	67	68	69	70
71	72	73	74	75	76	77	78	79	80
81	82	83	84	85	86	87	88	89	90
91	92	93	94	95	96	97	98	99	100

Color all the even numbers on this chart. Start with **2**, **4**, and **6**. Continue coloring and counting by 2s all the way up to 100. Read the even numbers out loud as fast as you can. Then read the odd numbers!

Math Skill: Identifying odd and even numbers using skip-counting

MATH

Count on It

Number charts can come in pretty handy. Follow the directions to try some new ways of counting.

1	2	3	4	5	6	7	8	9	10
11	12	13	14	15	16	17	18	19	20
21	22	23	24	25	26	27	28	29	30
31	32	33	34	35	36	37	38	39	40
41	42	43	44	45	46	47	48	49	50
51	52	53	54	55	56	57	58	59	60
61	62	63	64	65	66	67	68	69	70
71	72	73	74	75	76	77	78	79	80
81	82	83	84	85	86	87	88	89	90
91	92	93	94	95	96	97	98	99	100

- Count by 10s. Use the chart to help you.

  ____ ____ ____ ____ ____

  ____ ____ ____ ____ ____

- Where were all the 10s on the chart?

  _____

- Count by 5s. Write the numbers here.

  ____ ____ ____ ____ ____

  ____ ____ ____ ____ ____

  ____ ____ ____ ____ ____

  ____ ____ ____ ____ ____

- Are all the numbers odd or even when you count by 10? _____
- Are all the numbers odd or even when you count by 5? _____

How about this? Can you solve this brain-twister? I am a number in the top half of the hundred chart. I am odd. If you add the digit in the ones place to the digit in the tens place, you get 5. The number in the ones place is one larger than the number in the tens place.

Math Skill: Using skip-counting to count by 5s and 10s

MATH

Ones, Tens, and Hundreds

Here's one way to show the number 329.

- Find the ones. How many are there? _____

- How many tens are there? _____

- How many ones are there in one ten? _____

- How many hundreds are there? _____

- How many tens in one block of one hundred? _____

Write a number for each picture.

_____

_____

_____

Math Skill: Understanding place value of ones, tens, and hundreds

70

MATH

More Ones, Tens, and Hundreds

Draw a line from each picture to the number it shows.

212

312

322

163

444

424

Math Skill: Understanding place value of ones, tens, hundreds

MATH

Quick Draw

These pictures don't fit the numbers! Add more blocks to the pictures so they match.

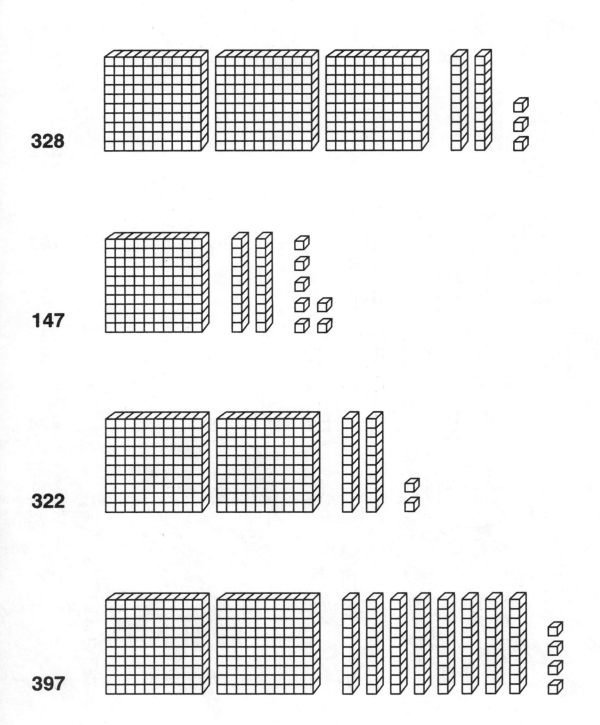

328

147

322

397

Math Skill: Understanding place value of ones, tens, hundreds

MATH

Let's Try Thousands

You could count thousands and thousands of stars in the sky. A thousand is 10 hundreds. We write it 1,000. One way to show 1,000 is in a block like this one. Each layer is a hundred. Count the layers to make sure there are 10 hundreds here! Then try to figure out some questions about numbers in the thousands.

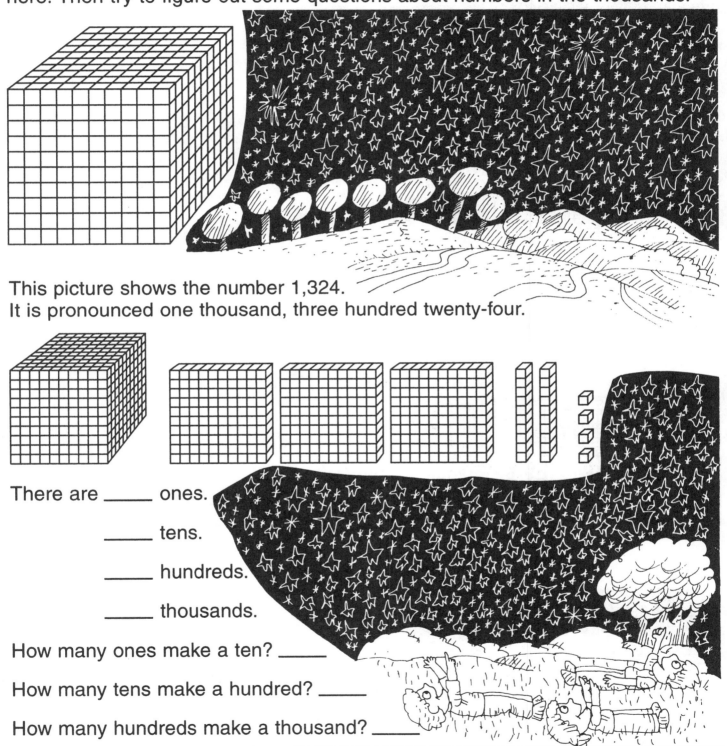

This picture shows the number 1,324.
It is pronounced one thousand, three hundred twenty-four.

There are _____ ones.

_____ tens.

_____ hundreds.

_____ thousands.

How many ones make a ten? _____

How many tens make a hundred? _____

How many hundreds make a thousand? _____

Math Skill: Understanding place value of ones, tens, hundreds, thousands

MATH

The Numbers Keep Getting Bigger

Anything you can do with hundreds, you can do with thousands! Can you fill in these **place-value charts**? The first one is done for you.

hundreds	tens	ones
2	6	8

hundreds	tens	ones
_____	_____	_____

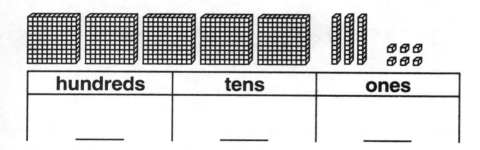

one thousands	hundreds	tens	ones
_____ ,	_____	_____	_____

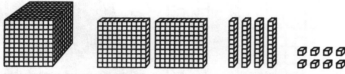

one thousands	hundreds	tens	ones
_____ ,	_____	_____	_____

Math Skill: Understanding place value of ones, tens, hundreds, and thousands

MATH

Really Big Numbers!
Dr. Whizbang has been counting the stars in the sky. He's getting very big numbers for his answers. Do you know any really big numbers? Compare the two place-value charts. Answer the questions. Then you'll be able to help Dr. Whizbang!

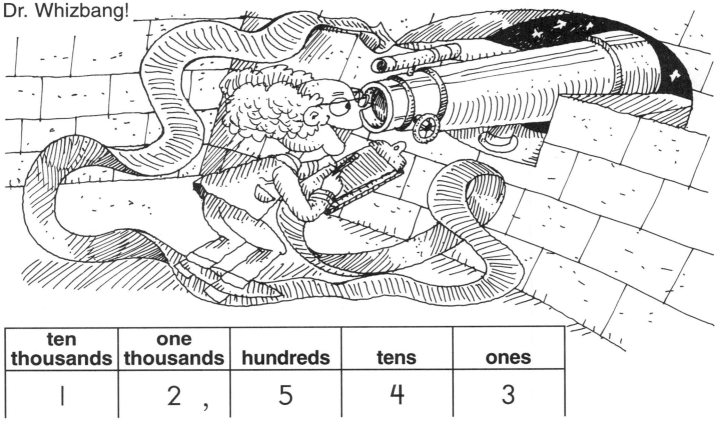

ten thousands	one thousands	hundreds	tens	ones
1	2 ,	5	4	3

We say **twelve thousand, five hundred forty-three**.

How would you write this number? _____

hundred thousands	ten thousands	one thousands	hundreds	tens	ones
2	3	4 ,	6	2	9

We say **two hundred thirty-four thousand, six hundred twenty-nine**.

How would you write this number? _____

How about this? *Read the newspaper or a magazine with a grown-up. Look for really big numbers in the stories, read them out loud, and talk about what they mean.*

Math Skill: Understanding place value up to the hundred thousands

MATH

More Giant Numbers

There are lots of fun things to do with big numbers. Try these!
Read the words. Then add more numbers.

twenty-five

2 ____

three hundred twenty-five

32 ____

four thousand, three hundred twenty-five

4, _____

twenty-four thousand, three hundred twenty-five

24, _____

one hundred twenty-four thousand, three hundred twenty-five

124, _____

Circle the largest number in each set.

35	421	1,295	10,843	321,000
53	666	9,295	10,999	123,000
42	667	8,298	9,421	231,000

How about this? Build numbers with a family member. Begin with a one-digit number like
6. Keep adding tens, hundreds, and so on. Every time you add a digit, you have to read the
number out loud. It's not easy, but you can do it.

Math Skill: Exploring place-value with larger numbers

MATH

Rounding

Your mom wants to know how many people went to Alberto's party. It's not easy to remember. "I don't need an exact number!" says Mom. "You can **round**." That makes it easier! You can tell her there were **about 10** people there. But it could have been 11 or 9.

Rounding Rules

- If the number is 5 or above, round up to the nearest 10.
- If it's below 5, round to the lower 10.
- The same goes for 100. If it's 50 or over, round up to the nearest 100.
- If it's below 50, round down to the nearest 100.

Circle the number that is closer.

58—round up to 60 or down to 50?

23—round up to 30 or down to 20?

25—round up to 30 or down to 20?

97—round up to 100 or down to 90?

224—round up to 300 or down to 200?

578—round up to 600 or down to 500?

Math Skill: Rounding to the nearest ten or one hundred

MATH

A "ROUND" the House
Fill in the blanks with tens or hundreds.

Moe: There were 98 guests at my party. So if I were to round, I'd say there were _____ guests.

Toe: I was at your party. I think there were exactly 23 guests. So if I were to round, I'd say there were about _____ guests.

Moe: You are way off. I counted 57 people in my coat closet alone. That is about _____ people.

Toe: You must be dreaming. I counted 12 people with coats. That is about _____.

Moe: My guests ate 793 cupcakes at the party. That is about _____ cupcakes.

Toe: I didn't see cupcakes. But the 172 squishy brown french fries I ate were really good. I couldn't believe I ate about _____ french fries.

Moe: I can't believe it either. Those were my worms for fishing!

How about this? *Look at bunches of things in your house but don't count them. Give a number rounded to ten or one hundred to tell about how many there are. For example, "There are about ten cookies on the plate, about 100 napkins in the package."*

Math Skill: Rounding to the nearest ten or hundred

MATH

Adding It Up

Adding big numbers can be tricky! But you'll be fine if you remember to add the ones column first, and then the tens column. Look at this example.

Add the ones: **Add the tens**:

```
 tens ones          tens ones
  2    3             2    3
+ 3    4           + 3    4
────────           ────────
       7             5    7
```

The ones have been added for you. Check the answers. Circle and correct any that are wrong! Then add the tens.

```
 32      26      29      36      68      10      55      85
+45     +13     +40     +21     +21     +20     +34     +14
───      ───     ───     ───     ───     ───     ───     ───
  7       9       9       7       9       0       9       9
```

Try these on your own.

```
 50      85      20      77      63      89      24      45      27
+49     +12     +30     +11     +33     +10     +44     +42     +72
───      ───     ───     ───     ───     ───     ───     ───     ───
```

How about this? *Brunhilde wanted to know how many cartons of milk she drank in two months. So she saved the empty cartons under her bed. Boy, was her mom mad. The first month Brunhilde saved 13 milk cartons. The next month she saved a whopping 64 cartons. How many cartons were there all together under that bed?*

Math Skill: Adding 2-digit numbers without regrouping

MATH

Adding Is Trickier than You Thought

Even math masters get stumped sometimes. Try this problem:

Add the ones:

```
  2 6
+ 1 8
  1 4
```

But wait! 14 is too big for the ones column! What do you do? Let's think. Remember that 14 can be written as 1 ten and 4 ones. This is called **regrouping**.

Since the 1 is actually a 10, you can add the 1 to the top of the tens column! We say you **carry** the 1. Look:

Carry the one:

```
 +1
  2 6
+ 1 8
  (0)4
```

Now add the tens:

```
+1
  2 6
+ 1 8
  4 4
```

Try these. First trace over the regrouped answer from the ones column. Then add the tens.

```
+1            +1            +1
 73            35            56
+18           +45           +19
  1             0             5
```

Add these numbers. Don't forget to regroup.

```
 17      24      37      35
+17     +69     +26     +25
```

```
 49      27      34      84
+39     +18     +57     +16
```

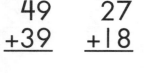

How about this? *Tony is making a fort. He found 19 big cardboard boxes and 13 little boxes. "I don't think you need that many boxes," said Tony's dad. "You never know," said Tony. How many boxes did Tony find all together?*

Math Skill: Adding 2-digit numbers with regrouping

80

MATH

Don't Just Take a Wild Guess

Do you remember how to **round**? Rounding is an easy way to guess **about** how much the answer should be when you add or subtract. You don't choose an exact number! This is called **estimating**.

Let's estimate this problem to the nearest ten.

38	rounds up to 40.	40
+21	rounds down to 20.	+20

40 + 20 = 60! The **estimated** answer is 60.
Can you figure out how close that is to the real answer?

Look at the problems below. Don't give the exact answer. Estimate the answers to the nearest 10. Then go back and figure out the exact answer. How close are the two answers?

```
 12          32          41          57
+19    + ___ +38   + ___ +36   + ___ +33   + ___


 92          39          23          61
-54    - ___ -17   - ___ + 7   + ___ -24   - ___
```

Math Skill: Estimating sums and differences to the nearest 10

83

MATH

Adding Larger Numbers

If you know how to regroup, you can add a number that is a million digits long. Of course, why would you want to? Get a life! But adding a number 3 digits long can be fun. Watch the regrouping steps:

```
  546          +1            +1
+282          546          546
─────        +282         +282
   8         ─────        ─────
              28           828
```

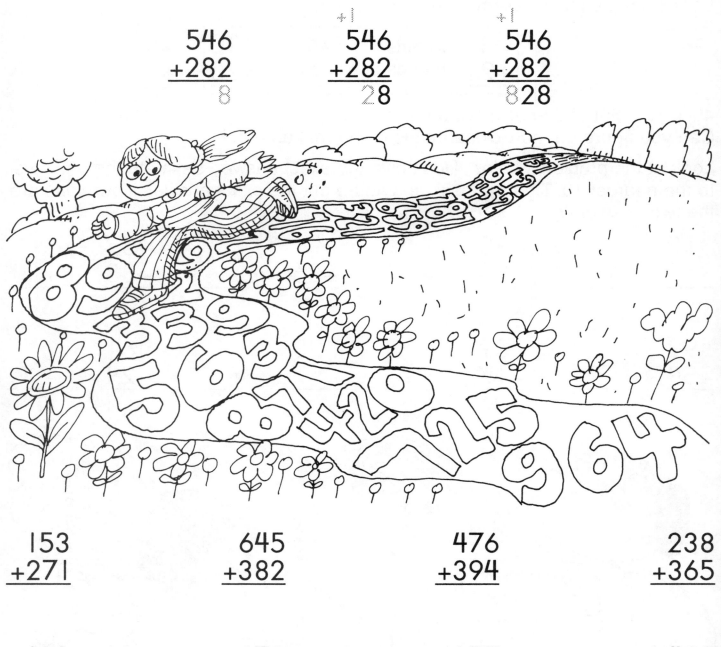

```
  153          645          476          238
+271         +382         +394         +365
─────        ─────        ─────        ─────


  123          672          857          429
+794         +278         +151         +190
─────        ─────        ─────        ─────
```

Math Skill: Adding 3-digit numbers with regrouping

MATH

Subtracting Larger Numbers

You can use regrouping to subtract ultra-long numbers. But you're a very busy kid. You only have time to subtract some three-digit numbers. Watch the regrouping steps:

$$
\begin{array}{r} 2 \\ \cancel{3}14 \\ -192 \\ \hline 2 \end{array}
\qquad
\begin{array}{r} 2\ 11 \\ \cancel{3}\cancel{1}4 \\ -192 \\ \hline 22 \end{array}
\qquad
\begin{array}{r} 2\ 11 \\ \cancel{3}\cancel{1}4 \\ -192 \\ \hline 122 \end{array}
$$

$$
\begin{array}{r} 527 \\ -182 \\ \hline \end{array}
\qquad
\begin{array}{r} 413 \\ -222 \\ \hline \end{array}
\qquad
\begin{array}{r} 659 \\ -181 \\ \hline \end{array}
\qquad
\begin{array}{r} 372 \\ -192 \\ \hline \end{array}
$$

$$
\begin{array}{r} 527 \\ -333 \\ \hline \end{array}
\qquad
\begin{array}{r} 476 \\ -192 \\ \hline \end{array}
\qquad
\begin{array}{r} 739 \\ -348 \\ \hline \end{array}
\qquad
\begin{array}{r} 613 \\ -240 \\ \hline \end{array}
$$

Math Skill: Subtracting 3-digit numbers with regrouping

Subtracting Across Zero

Sometimes a subtraction problem can throw you for a loop! There is only a zero in the tens column. What is a kid to do?

Try to subtract the ones. You can't subtract 6 from 2. So you go to the tens. But there aren't any. $\begin{array}{r} 702 \\ -156 \end{array}$	You take 1 of the hundreds. You regroup it as 10 tens. $\begin{array}{r} {}^{6}\cancel{7}\,{}^{10}\cancel{0}\,2 \\ -156 \end{array}$
You take one of the tens. You regroup it as 10 ones. $\begin{array}{r} {}^{9} \\ {}^{6}\cancel{7}\,\cancel{0}\,{}^{12}\cancel{2} \\ -156 \end{array}$	Now you can subtract! $\begin{array}{r} {}^{9} \\ {}^{6}\cancel{7}\,\cancel{0}\,{}^{12}\cancel{2} \\ -156 \\ \hline 546 \end{array}$

Now you try it. Complete the subtraction problems.

$\begin{array}{r} 905 \\ -156 \\ \hline \end{array}$
$\begin{array}{r} 504 \\ -265 \\ \hline \end{array}$
$\begin{array}{r} 408 \\ -279 \\ \hline \end{array}$
$\begin{array}{r} 603 \\ -414 \\ \hline \end{array}$
$\begin{array}{r} 802 \\ -124 \\ \hline \end{array}$
$\begin{array}{r} 606 \\ -301 \\ \hline \end{array}$

$\begin{array}{r} 204 \\ -198 \\ \hline \end{array}$
$\begin{array}{r} 103 \\ -\ 99 \\ \hline \end{array}$
$\begin{array}{r} 603 \\ -595 \\ \hline \end{array}$
$\begin{array}{r} 604 \\ -176 \\ \hline \end{array}$
$\begin{array}{r} 507 \\ -278 \\ \hline \end{array}$
$\begin{array}{r} 902 \\ -555 \\ \hline \end{array}$

How about this? *Here is a problem that is a little harder: 500 − 173. How is it different from the problems you just completed? How would you find the answer? Who in your family would understand how smart you were to figure it out?*

Math Skill: Subtracting across zeros

MATH

Multiplying with 2 Groups

Adding is something like multiplying. This picture shows 2 groups of 3. You already know one way to write it: 3 + 3 = 6. But there's another way to write it, using multiplication. Since you have 2 groups of 3 socks, you can write:

number of groups	number in each group
2 ×	3 = 6.

We say **2 times 3 equals 6**. Try the problems below. Say them out loud when you are done. The answer in multiplication is sometimes called the **product**.

4 + 4 = __	5 + 5 = __	6 + 6 = __
2 × 4 = __	2 × 5 = __	2 × 6 = __
7 + 7 = __	8 + 8 = __	9 + 9 = __
2 × 7 = __	2 × 8 = __	2 × 9 = __

Mallard has 2 piles of laundry. There are 5 shirts in each pile. Follow the directions below to learn more about Mallard and all of his dirty shirts.

- Write an addition sentence to show how many shirts he has. _____

- Write a multiplication sentence to show how many shirts he has. _____

Math Skill: Multiplying by 2

MATH

Special Multiplication with 1 and 0

When you multiply any number times 1, you get the same number. For example:

number of groups	number in each group		
1	× 3	=	3.

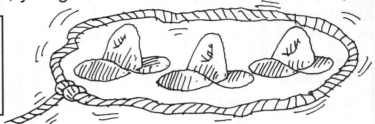

When you multiply by zero, the answer is always zero.

number of groups	number in each group		
0	× 3	=	0.

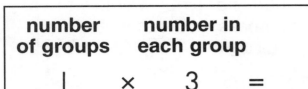

Multiply these special problems.

$$
\begin{array}{ccccccccccc}
9 & 8 & 7 & 6 & 5 & 4 & 3 & 2 & 1 & 0 \\
\times 1 & \times 1 & \times 1 & \times 1 & \times 1 & \times 1 & \times 1 & \times 1 & \times 1 & \times 1
\end{array}
$$

$$
\begin{array}{ccccccccccc}
9 & 8 & 7 & 6 & 5 & 4 & 3 & 2 & 1 & 0 \\
\times 0 & \times 0 & \times 0 & \times 0 & \times 0 & \times 0 & \times 0 & \times 0 & \times 0 & \times 0
\end{array}
$$

How about this? Write a story in which some silly people go shopping 2 times. One person buys 3 things each time, one person buys 6 things each time, one person buys 1 thing each time, and one person buys 0 things each time.

Math Skill: Multiplying by 0 and 1

MATH

Multiplying with 3 Groups

There are snails all over the sidewalk! Let's look at this picture as addition and as multiplication. We can write 4 + 4 + 4 = 12. Or we can write:

number of groups	number in each group		
3	× 4	=	12.

Let's look at the pictures a little differently.
We can write 3 + 3 + 3 + 3 = 12. Or we can write:

number of groups	number in each group		
4	× 3	=	12.

Try these addition and multiplication problems.

5 + 5 + 5 = ___	7 + 7 + 7 = ___	2 + 2 + 2 = ___
3 × 5 = ___	3 × 7 = ___	3 × 2 = ___
5 × 3 = ___	7 × 3 = ___	2 × 3 = ___
3 × 2 = ___	3 × 6 = ___	3 × 9 = ___
2 × 3 = ___	6 × 3 = ___	9 × 3 = ___
3 × 8 = ___	3 × 1 = ___	3 × 0 = ___
8 × 3 = ___	1 × 3 = ___	0 × 3 = ___

How about this? *Draw a picture that shows 3 x 5 = 15. Circle the groups of 3. Then draw a picture that shows 5 x 3 = 15. Circle the groups of 5.*

Math Skill: Multiplying by 3 using the order property

MATH

Multiplying with Four Groups

Maggie, Millie, Molly, and May have 5 seashells each. We can write
5 + 5 + 5 + 5 = 20. Fill in the blanks to write it as a multiplication sentence.

number of groups		number in each group		
__4__	×	_____	=	_____.

HERE'S WHAT WE THINK · 4×5=20 SO, 5×4=20, TOO!

Add or multiply.

2 + 2 + 2 + 2 = ____   6 + 6 + 6 + 6 = ____   9 + 9 + 9 + 9 = ____

4 × 2 = ____   4 × 6 = ____   4 × 9 = ____

2 × 4 = ____   6 × 4 = ____   9 × 4 = ____

Multiplication can be written in a different way. Try these!

$$\begin{array}{r} 2 \\ \times 4 \\ \hline \end{array} \qquad \begin{array}{r} 3 \\ \times 4 \\ \hline \end{array} \qquad \begin{array}{r} 5 \\ \times 4 \\ \hline \end{array} \qquad \begin{array}{r} 0 \\ \times 4 \\ \hline \end{array} \qquad \begin{array}{r} 1 \\ \times 4 \\ \hline \end{array} \qquad \begin{array}{r} 7 \\ \times 4 \\ \hline \end{array}$$

Math Skill: Multiplying by 4 in different orders and formats

MATH

Multiplying with 5 Groups

It's a rabbit's delight! Can you write the adding sentence that explains this picture? Then try to write the multiplying sentence.

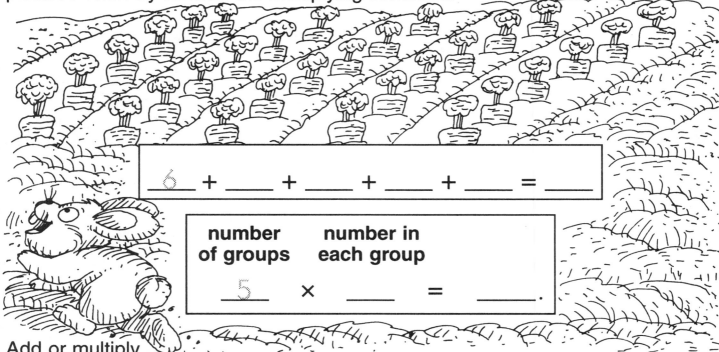

6 + ___ + ___ + ___ + ___ = ___

number of groups		number in each group	
_5_	×	___	= ___ .

Add or multiply.

2+2+2+2+2 = ___   3+3+3+3+3 = ___   4+4+4+4+4 = ___

5 × 2 = ___   5 × 3 = ___   5 × 4 = ___

2 × 5 = ___   3 × 5 = ___   4 × 5 = ___

5 × 5 = ___   5 × 6 = ___   5 × 1 = ___

5 × 0 = ___   5 × 7 = ___   5 × 8 = ___

6	5	8	5	1	5	9	9	9	9	9	9
×5	×6	×5	×8	×5	×1	×1	×2	×3	×4	×5	×0

How about this? Ask your friends which they would rather have: 1 times 17 dollars, or 0 times a trillion dollars?

Math Skill: Using multiplication with factors from 0 through 5

MATH

The Multiplication Table

Jamila knows that she'll multiply faster if she can remember the multiplication facts from 0 to 9. Look at the multiplication table she wrote to help her memory.

	0	1	2	3	4	5	6	7	8	9
0	0	0	0	0	0	0	0	0	0	0
1	0	1	2	3	4	5	6	7	8	9
2	0	2	4	6	8	10	12	14	16	18
3	0	3	6	9	12	15	18	21	24	27
4	0	4	8	12	16	20	24	28	32	36
5	0	5	10	15	20	25	30	35	40	45
6	0	6	12	18	24	30	36	42	48	54
7	0	7	14	21	28	35	42	49	56	63
8	0	8	16	24	32	40	48	56	64	72
9	0	9	18	27	36	45	54	63	72	81

Here is Jamila's trick for using the table to find answers:

- Think of a problem, like 8 × 6.

- Move a finger from your left hand down to the beginning of the 8 row. It is shaded. Start to slide your finger across the row.

- Move a finger from your right hand across to the beginning of the 6 column. It is shaded. Start to slide your finger down the column.

- Stop when your fingers meet. What number is under your fingers? 48! That's the answer!

Use the chart to answer these problems.

$$\begin{array}{r} 7 \\ \times 7 \\ \hline \end{array} \qquad \begin{array}{r} 4 \\ \times 9 \\ \hline \end{array} \qquad \begin{array}{r} 8 \\ \times 3 \\ \hline \end{array} \qquad \begin{array}{r} 7 \\ \times 8 \\ \hline \end{array} \qquad \begin{array}{r} 8 \\ \times 9 \\ \hline \end{array} \qquad \begin{array}{r} 5 \\ \times 0 \\ \hline \end{array}$$

How about this? *You can make a multiplication table of your own! Then you can carry it wherever you go. You'll never be stuck on a hard problem again!*

Math Skill: Using a multiplication table

MATH

6 Times, 7 Times, 8 Times!

Use the multiplication table to solve these problems about groups of 6, 7, and 8.

$$\begin{array}{r} 3 \\ \times 6 \\ \hline \end{array} \qquad \begin{array}{r} 8 \\ \times 2 \\ \hline \end{array} \qquad \begin{array}{r} 8 \\ \times 6 \\ \hline \end{array} \qquad \begin{array}{r} 2 \\ \times 7 \\ \hline \end{array} \qquad \begin{array}{r} 7 \\ \times 0 \\ \hline \end{array}$$

$$\begin{array}{r} 6 \\ \times 4 \\ \hline \end{array} \qquad \begin{array}{r} 8 \\ \times 7 \\ \hline \end{array} \qquad \begin{array}{r} 7 \\ \times 6 \\ \hline \end{array} \qquad \begin{array}{r} 6 \\ \times 7 \\ \hline \end{array} \qquad \begin{array}{r} 8 \\ \times 5 \\ \hline \end{array}$$

$$\begin{array}{r} 6 \\ \times 1 \\ \hline \end{array} \qquad \begin{array}{r} 4 \\ \times 8 \\ \hline \end{array} \qquad \begin{array}{r} 8 \\ \times 9 \\ \hline \end{array} \qquad \begin{array}{r} 9 \\ \times 7 \\ \hline \end{array} \qquad \begin{array}{r} 8 \\ \times 8 \\ \hline \end{array}$$

Did Hiram solve these problems correctly? Use the chart to check his answers. Circle a problem if the answer is right. If the answer is wrong, cross it out and write the correct answer next to it.

$$\begin{array}{r} 1 \\ \times 8 \\ \hline 8 \end{array} \qquad \begin{array}{r} 5 \\ \times 6 \\ \hline 30 \end{array} \qquad \begin{array}{r} 7 \\ \times 3 \\ \hline 21 \end{array}$$

$$\begin{array}{r} 3 \\ \times 8 \\ \hline 24 \end{array} \qquad \begin{array}{r} 4 \\ \times 7 \\ \hline 30 \end{array} \qquad \begin{array}{r} 0 \\ \times 6 \\ \hline 6 \end{array}$$

Math Skill: Multiplying by 6, 7, and 8

MATH

Finger Math Fun

Imagine this: you have a big problem to solve with multiplying by 9—but the dog ate your multiplication table! Never mind. You have your fingers. And that's all you need to multiply by 9. Think of the fingers of your hands numbered like this:

To solve 9 × 4, here's what you do:

- Fold down finger number 4.
- Count the fingers showing on the left.
- Write that number on the left.
- Count the numbers on the right.
- Write that number on the right.
- Read your answer!

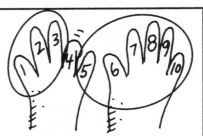

3 fingers 6 fingers

→**36**

9 × 4 = 36

Do the finger math. Write a multiplication sentence for each picture.

  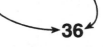

__9__ × ____ = ____   __9__ × ____ = ____   __9__ × ____ = ____

__9__ × ____ = ____   __9__ × ____ = ____

How about this? *The 9 times table is really amazing! Write down all the multiplication sentences for 9, with the answers. Then look hard at the answers. For 18, add 1 + 8. What do you get? For 27, add 2 + 7. What do you get? Try this for all the answers!*

Math Skill: Multiplying with a factor of 9

94

MATH

Let's Try Division

You know that this picture shows the multiplication sentence **2 × 5 = 10**. It also shows division! It says that if you split 10 strawberries into 2 equal groups, then each group will have 5 strawberries. We write this **10 ÷ 2 = 5**. The answer in a division problem is called a **quotient**.

Look at the pictures of beads and stamps below. Solve the multiplication problems they show. Then write a division problem that matches. You can look at a multiplication table for clues if you want!

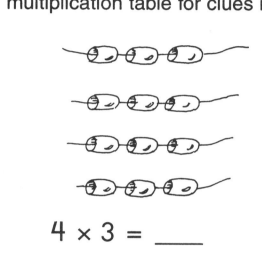 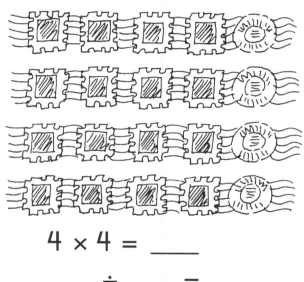

4 × 3 = _____

_____ ÷ _____ = _____

4 × 4 = _____

_____ ÷ _____ = _____

Multiply and divide. Draw pictures on some scrap paper if you want to.

4 × 5 = _____	4 × 7 = _____	4 × 9 = _____	4 × 6 = _____
20 ÷ 4 = _____	28 ÷ 4 = _____	36 ÷ 9 = _____	24 ÷ 4 = _____
2 × 3 = _____	2 × 9 = _____	2 × 7 = _____	2 × 8 = _____
6 ÷ 2 = _____	18 ÷ 2 = _____	14 ÷ 2 = _____	16 ÷ 2 = _____

How about this? *There are 20 students in Ms. Goodheart's class. Every one of them wants a part in the play. "Choose me," everyone yells. So Ms. Goodheart divided the class into 4 groups. Each group will present its own play. How many students will there be in each group?*

Math Skill: Understanding simple division

MATH

Same Amount, Different Groups

Do you remember that 3 × 2 is the same as 2 × 3? Division has a trick of its own. Look at these two pictures. Read their multiplication and division problems. Do you see how the two pictures are different?

$$3 \times 2 = 6$$
$$6 \div 2 = 3$$

$$2 \times 3 = 6$$
$$6 \div 3 = 2$$

Find the answers to these multiplication and division fact families.

2 × 4 = ___	3 × 6 = ___	4 × 8 = ___	4 × 9 = ___	3 × 5 = ___
4 × 2 = ___	6 × 3 = ___	8 × 4 = ___	9 × 4 = ___	5 × 3 = ___
8 ÷ 2 = ___	18 ÷ 3 = ___	32 ÷ 4 = ___	36 ÷ 4 = ___	15 ÷ 3 = ___
8 ÷ 4 = ___	18 ÷ 6 = ___	32 ÷ 8 = ___	36 ÷ 9 = ___	15 ÷ 5 = ___

How about this? *Get a pile of checkers, dominoes, buttons, candy, or anything else. Then see how many ways you can arrange them in even rows. Try to figure out the multiplication and division problems that show what you are doing.*

Math Skill: Dividing using fact families

MATH

Fact Families
Tammy and Jimmy John have about a million marbles! They are splitting them up into lots of different piles. Each time they split up a pile into a bunch of smaller piles, it's like doing a division problem. Help them by finding the answers below.

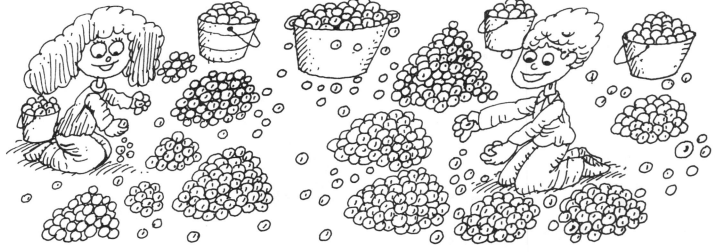

5 × 6 = ___	7 × 4 = ___	3 × 8 = ___	9 × 2 = ___
6 × 5 = ___	4 × 7 = ___	8 × 3 = ___	2 × 9 = ___
30 ÷ 6 = ___	28 ÷ 4 = ___	24 ÷ 8 = ___	18 ÷ 2 = ___
30 ÷ 5 = ___	28 ÷ 7 = ___	24 ÷ 3 = ___	18 ÷ 9 = ___
6 × 9 = ___	7 × 8 = ___	9 × 7 = ___	6 × 7 = ___
9 × 6 = ___	8 × 7 = ___	7 × 9 = ___	7 × 6 = ___
54 ÷ 9 = ___	56 ÷ 8 = ___	63 ÷ 7 = ___	42 ÷ 7 = ___
54 ÷ 6 = ___	56 ÷ 7 = ___	63 ÷ 9 = ___	42 ÷ 6 = ___

How about this? *Get a fresh piece of paper and draw a picture story. Include you and 23 friends. Color the shirts to show 4 different teams. One team has just won a race! Draw a trophy held by each kid on the winning team. How many trophies will you need to draw?*

Math Skill: Dividing using fact families

MATH

A Challenge!
Look at the problems below. You can probably tell that something is missing—the math sign! Can you write the correct sign in the circle to make a true math fact? This is hard, but it's worth a try!

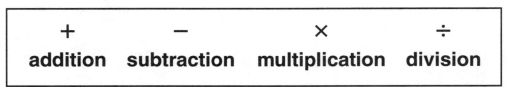

+	−	×	÷
addition	subtraction	multiplication	division

6 ◯ 8 = 48	2 ◯ 2 = 1	3 ◯ 2 = 4	2 ◯ 2 = 0
2 ◯ 3 = 6	3 ◯ 1 = 4	6 ◯ 2 = 3	4 ◯ 5 = 20
12 ◯ 3 = 4	7 ◯ 2 = 14	5 ◯ 7 = 12	18 ◯ 6 = 12
8 ◯ 2 = 10	8 ◯ 2 = 6	8 ◯ 2 = 16	8 ◯ 2 = 4
20 ◯ 6 = 14	20 ◯ 3 = 23	20 ◯ 2 = 10	20 ◯ 10 = 30

How about this? *Here's a trick question! What sign should you write to complete the number fact 2 ◯ 2 = 4? Hint: there are 2 correct answers!*

Math Skill: Understanding addition, subtraction, multiplication, and division

MATH

It's Raining Cats and Dogs

Read these division sentences. Draw a picture on some scrap paper to show what is happening in each sentence. Then write the answer on the line.

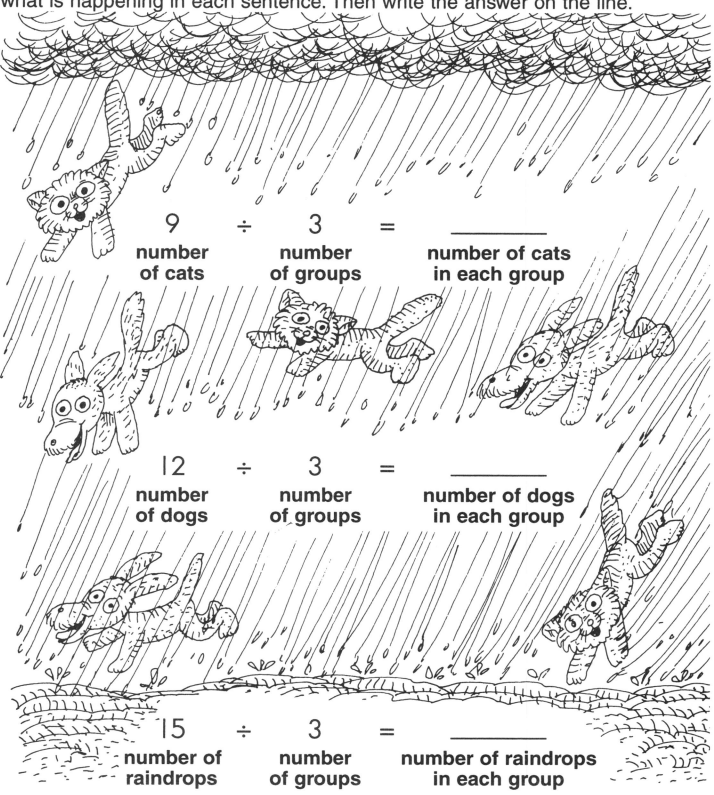

9 ÷ 3 = _____

| number
of cats | number
of groups | number of cats
in each group |

12 ÷ 3 = _____

| number
of dogs | number
of groups | number of dogs
in each group |

15 ÷ 3 = _____

| number of
raindrops | number
of groups | number of raindrops
in each group |

Math Skill: Understanding simple division facts

Division Decoder

There are secret messages being sent all around you. Complete the division charts below. Each answer matches a letter. Use your answers to decode the message!

Divide the numbers in the top row by 2:

÷	0	2	4	6	8	10	12	14	16	18	20
2	0	1	2	3							
	T	W	E	B	A	S	H	O	M	I	R

Divide the numbers in the top row by 6:

÷	0	6	12	18	24	30	36	42	48	54	60
6											
	T	W	E	B	A	S	H	O	M	I	R

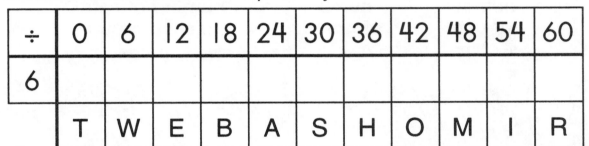

Solve the code to find out what this outer-space visitor is asking:

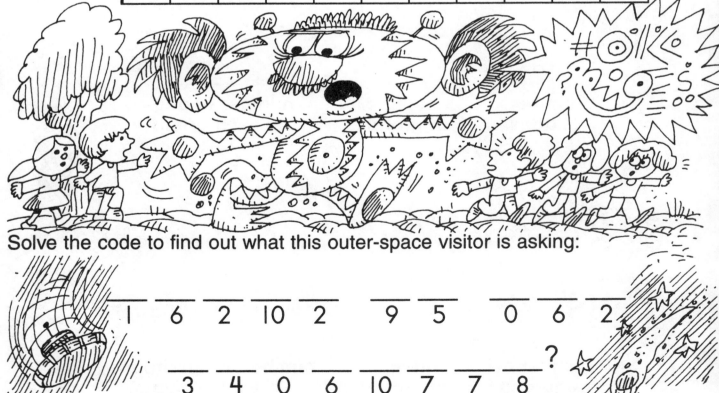

1 6 2 10 2   9 5   0 6 2
——————————————————————————— ?
3 4 0 6 10 7 7 8

Math Skill: Exploring division facts

MATH

Look Sharp!

Mickey just finished his math homework. Will you check his work? Look at the answers he circled. If he is right, put a star next to the problem. If he is wrong, circle the right answer!

7 ×9 54 (63) 56	2 ×8 16 28 (14)	4 ×4 18 8 (16)	3 ×8 (22) 24 38
5 ×6 25 30 (35)	7 ×3 20 (21) 22	2 ×6 12 26 (10)	7 ×4 (21) 28 27

36 ÷ 9 =	5	(4)	3
25 ÷ 5 =	5	4	(6)
18 ÷ 2 =	(6)	3	9
20 ÷ 4 =	4	6	(5)
42 ÷ 7 =	7	(8)	6
54 ÷ 6 =	(9)	8	6
32 ÷ 4 =	8	6	(9)
45 ÷ 5 =	(9)	4	8
72 ÷ 9 =	7	(8)	2

How about this? You can check your own homework by reading the problems out loud to your Mom or Dad. If you find any mistakes, you can fix them on the spot!

Math Skill: Multiplying and dividing using 1-digit factors

MATH

Greater Than, Less Than
The math signs > and < are an easy way to show which number is bigger. Here is how they work:

The wide open part always faces the bigger number. We write **6 >1**. We say **six is greater than one**.

The pointing end always points to the smaller number. We write **3 < 8**. We say **three is less than eight**.

Write < or > in the ◯. Say the words **greater than** or **less than** to yourself as you make the sign.

6 ◯ 2

2 ◯ 6

57 ◯ 91

91 ◯ 57

100 ◯ 10

45 ◯ 50

17 ◯ 13

3 ◯ 0

343 ◯ 444

175 ◯ 172

848 ◯ 745

1,000 ◯ 1,222

Math Skill: Using > (greater than) and < (less than) signs

MATH

It All Measures Up

Sometimes, one side is the same as the other side, even if it doesn't look the same. For example, **2 + 4** and **3 × 2** have the same answer: **6**! That means that **2 + 4 = 3 × 2**. Look at the number sentences below. If the two sides are equal, write = in the ◯. If one side is bigger than the other, write < or >.

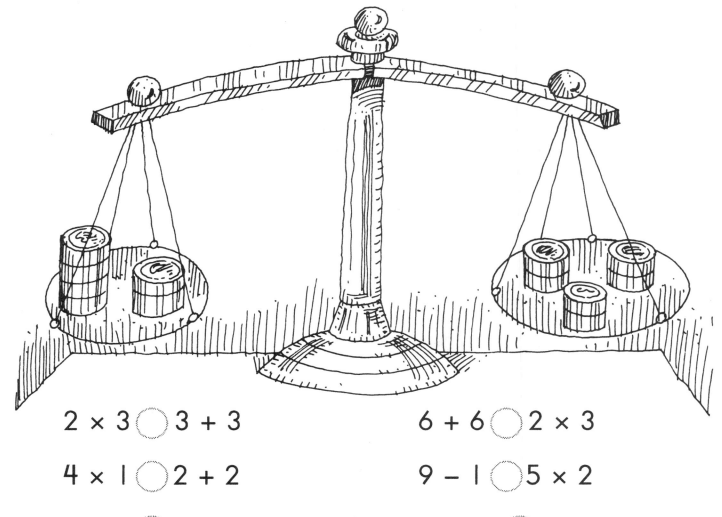

2 × 3 ◯ 3 + 3   6 + 6 ◯ 2 × 3

4 × 1 ◯ 2 + 2   9 – 1 ◯ 5 × 2

2 × 4 ◯ 4 + 4   12 – 3 ◯ 10 – 2

5 – 1 ◯ 2 + 2   9 × 0 ◯ 0 × 0

4 × 4 ◯ 5 × 5   5 × 4 ◯ 30 – 10

8 × 8 ◯ 9 × 9   2 × 6 ◯ 3 × 4

Math Skill: Using > (greater than) and < (less than) signs with algebraic thinking

103

MATH

Multiplying Larger Numbers

You can figure out what 3 × 3 is by using a multiplication table, or by using your memory. But can you figure out what 3 × 23 is?

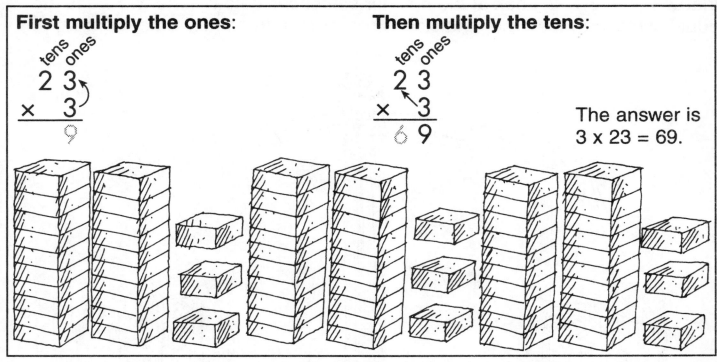

First multiply the ones:

tens ones
2 3
×   3
9

Then multiply the tens:

tens ones
2 3
×   3
6 9

The answer is
3 x 23 = 69.

Look at the problems below. The ones have been multiplied for you. Trace the answer in the ones column. Then multiply the tens.

$$\begin{array}{r} 23 \\ \times\ 3 \\ \hline 9 \end{array} \qquad \begin{array}{r} 10 \\ \times\ 6 \\ \hline 0 \end{array} \qquad \begin{array}{r} 22 \\ \times\ 4 \\ \hline 8 \end{array} \qquad \begin{array}{r} 11 \\ \times\ 5 \\ \hline 5 \end{array} \qquad \begin{array}{r} 42 \\ \times\ 2 \\ \hline 4 \end{array}$$

Look at the problems below. First multiply the ones. Then multiply the tens.

$$\begin{array}{r} 33 \\ \times\ 3 \\ \hline \end{array} \qquad \begin{array}{r} 24 \\ \times\ 2 \\ \hline \end{array} \qquad \begin{array}{r} 14 \\ \times\ 2 \\ \hline \end{array} \qquad \begin{array}{r} 31 \\ \times\ 3 \\ \hline \end{array} \qquad \begin{array}{r} 11 \\ \times\ 6 \\ \hline \end{array} \qquad \begin{array}{r} 44 \\ \times\ 2 \\ \hline \end{array}$$

$$\begin{array}{r} 47 \\ \times\ 2 \\ \hline \end{array} \qquad \begin{array}{r} 81 \\ \times\ 6 \\ \hline \end{array} \qquad \begin{array}{r} 72 \\ \times\ 4 \\ \hline \end{array} \qquad \begin{array}{r} 83 \\ \times\ 3 \\ \hline \end{array} \qquad \begin{array}{r} 62 \\ \times\ 4 \\ \hline \end{array} \qquad \begin{array}{r} 91 \\ \times\ 9 \\ \hline \end{array}$$

Math Skill: Multiplying a 2-digit number by a 1-digit number

MATH

Dividing Larger Numbers

Mitzi is sharing her box of candy. There are 69 pieces of candy in the box. She needs to divide it into 3 equal groups. But 69 ÷ 3 is a hard division problem! To solve it, Mitzi will need to write it in a new way:

We say 3 into 69	First divide the tens.	Then divide the ones.	
$3\overline{)69}$	$6 \div 3 = 2$ $3\overline{)69}^{2}$	$9 \div 3 = 3$ $3\overline{)69}^{23}$	Mitzi's answer is 69 ÷ 3 = 23.

Try these division problems. Remember to divide the tens, and then the ones.

$3\overline{)39}$ $2\overline{)18}$ $2\overline{)68}$ $2\overline{)42}$

$4\overline{)88}$ $6\overline{)66}$ $7\overline{)70}$ $3\overline{)96}$

How about this? Brothers named Freak and Frank Frankenstein collected 84 dead bugs. They wanted to divide them into 2 equal groups. How many bugs did each brother get?

Math Skill: Dividing 2-digit numbers by 1-digit numbers in long division format

MATH

Life Just Got a Little Harder

Sometimes multiplication problems are tricky. Take a look at the problem below. It is making Ebenezer's eyes cross!

First multiply the ones. But 12 is too big to fit in the ones column! 23 × 4 12	Regroup it as 1 ten and 2 ones. Carry the 1 to the top of the tens column. +1 2 3 × 4 (1)2
Now multiply the tens. 4 × 2 = 8. But what do you do with the +1 at the top? +1 2 3 × 4 8 2	Add it to the answer in the tens column. 8 + 1 = 9. The answer is 92! +1 2 3 × 4 9 8 2

These problems are almost done. But Ebenezer forgot to add the number he carried. Please add it for him.

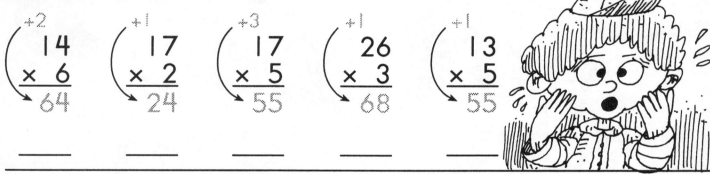

+2   +1   +3   +1   +1
 1 4   1 7   1 7   2 6   1 3
× 6   × 2   × 5   × 3   × 5
 64   24   55   68   55

___   ___   ___   ___   ___

Ebenezer has multiplied the ones column, regrouped the extra tens, and carried them over. Now multiply the tens column. Don't forget to add the number that Ebenezer carried over!

+1   +2   +4   +1   +2
 1 6   2 7   1 9   3 8   1 4
× 3   × 3   × 5   × 2   × 7
__8   __1   __5   __6   __8

Ebenezer is exhausted. Why don't you try these problems on your own? Don't forget to regroup and carry over the extra tens!

+___   +___   +___   +___   +___
 1 3   1 6   2 3   4 9   1 7
× 7   × 6   × 4   × 2   × 4

___   ___   ___   ___   ___

Math Skill: Multiplying a 2-digit number by a 1-digit number

MATH

Challenge the Master

Martin thinks he is the Math Master. Are you ready to challenge him? You'll need to stretch your brain a little. These multiplication problems have answers in the hundreds! Give them a try. The first one is done for you.

$$\begin{array}{r} 39 \\ \times\ 5 \\ \hline 195 \end{array} \qquad \begin{array}{r} 54 \\ \times\ 6 \\ \hline \end{array} \qquad \begin{array}{r} 39 \\ \times\ 4 \\ \hline \end{array} \qquad \begin{array}{r} 24 \\ \times\ 6 \\ \hline \end{array} \qquad \begin{array}{r} 32 \\ \times\ 9 \\ \hline \end{array}$$

Banner blew the best big bubbles. She decided to open a Bigger, Better Bubble School. I don't need to tell you, that takes a lot of bubble gum. Banner went to the gum store 4 times. Each time, she bought 36 pieces of bubble gum. How many pieces of gum did Banner have all together? Write this as a multiplication problem, and then solve it.

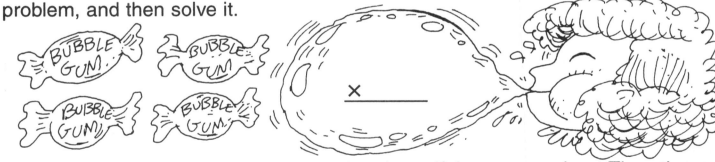

The owl and the pussycat went to sea in a beautiful pea-green boat. Then the pussycat said, "Oh, oh! I forgot my lunch." And the owl said, "I brought along enough birdseeds for each of us to have 76 for lunch. I will share them with you." How many birdseeds did the owl bring all together? Write this as a multiplication problem, and then solve it.

Math Skill: Multiplying a 2-digit number by a 1-digit number

MATH

Word Problems

Math shows up in the strangest places. Can you write down and solve math problems to answer the questions below? You will need to add, subtract, multiply, and divide.

The twins, Radiator and Carburetor, each have 25 toy racing cars. How many cars do they have all together?

Jack and Jill went up the hill 3 times every day for 5 days. How many times did they go up the hill?

Humpty-Dumpty sat on a wall that was 35 feet high. He fell 17 feet before he was caught by a friendly bird. How many feet above the sidewalk was Humpty when the bird caught him?

Your best friend Ka-floog-a-flunken wants to share equally 36 pennies with you. How many will you get?

You ordered a new bike. It will take 247 days to get to your house. 89 days have passed so far. How many more days do you have to wait?

What if you made 216 cookies each day for 4 days. How many cookies is that in all?

Math Skill: Understanding word problems using addition, subtraction, multiplication, and division

MATH

Parts of a Whole Thing

A **fraction** is a number that can name parts of a whole thing.

The number at the top tells how many parts are colored.
It is called the **numerator**.

The number at the bottom tells how many parts in all.
It is called the **denominator**.

$$\frac{1}{4}$$

Write a **fraction** for each picture. The first one is done for you.

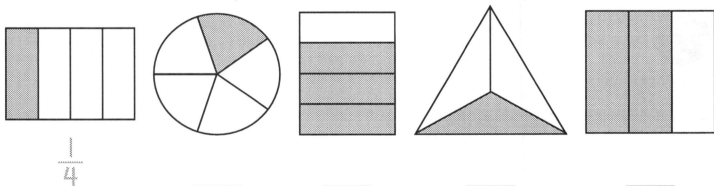

$$\frac{1}{4}$$

____   ____   ____   ____

Divide and color these shapes to show the fractions.

$$\frac{1}{4} \qquad \frac{3}{4} \qquad \frac{1}{2} \qquad \frac{5}{6}$$

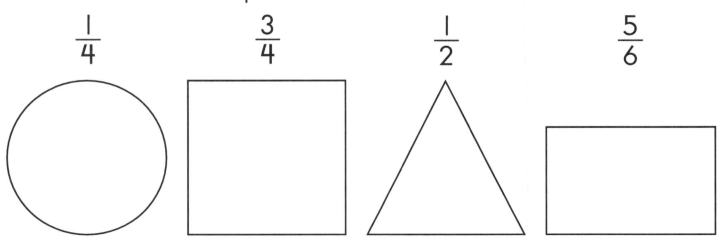

Math Skill: Understanding fractions as parts of a whole

Parts of a Group

Sometimes **fractions** name a part of a whole group. Compare the fractions with the pictures.

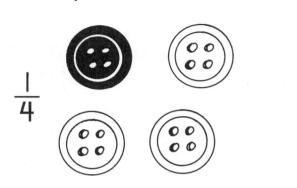

$\frac{1}{4}$

$\frac{3}{8}$

Write a fraction telling how many are colored in for each picture. The first one is done for you.

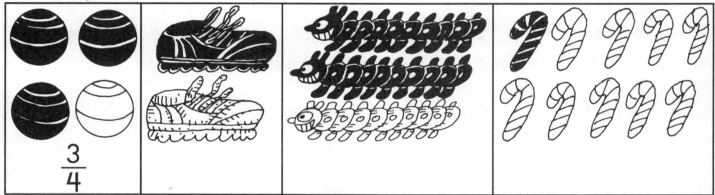

$\frac{3}{4}$

Look at the kids in this picture. How many kids are wearing caps? Write in the top number to tell how many.

$\overline{10}$

How about this? *Look at the picture of 10 kids again. Could you say that ½ of the kids are wearing caps? Why or why not? Tell a grown-up what you decide. Do you think that ⁵⁄₁₀ is the same as ½? How about ²⁄₄? ¾?*

Math Skill: Exploring fractions as parts of a group

110

MATH

Parts of a Whole and Group
Read the directions. Then color the pictures to show the **fractions**.

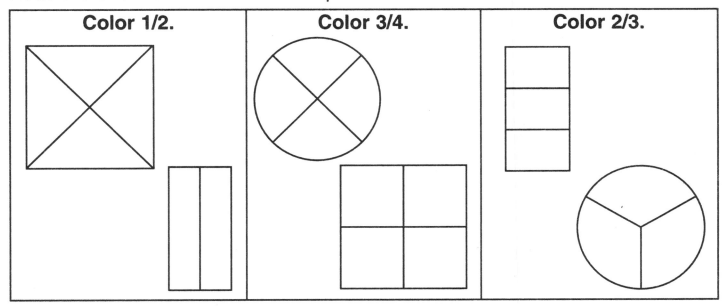

| Color 1/2. | Color 3/4. | Color 2/3. |

Color the pictures below to show the following fractions.

1 red clown in a group of 4 clowns

1 blue monster in a group of 3 monsters

2 green masks out of 4 masks

1 giant cake cut in 2 parts, with 1 part eaten

1 pepperoni pizza divided in 6 parts, but all the pepperoni picked off of 1 part

1 candy bar cut in 10 parts with 3 parts missing

Math Skill: Exploring parts of a whole and parts of a group

Decimals

You know that fractions can show numbers that are less than one—like ½ of a crayon. A **decimal** is another way to show numbers that are less than one. Decimals can show fractions of things that are divided into 10 parts.

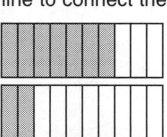

This shows ³⁄₁₀. We can also write it as **0.3.** and say it **three tenths**.

Draw a line to connect the right **fraction** to each picture. Then draw another line to connect the right **decimal** to the fraction!

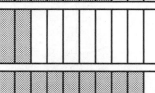

⁷⁄₁₀   0.7

⁹⁄₁₀   0.2

²⁄₁₀   0.9

Decimals fit into place value charts! They are smaller than the ones. We put a **decimal point** (.) in between the ones and the tenths. Here is the number twenty-three and four tenths:

tens	ones	tenths
2	3 .	4

23.4

Now fill in these place value charts. Then write the number on the blank. Don't forget to write the **decimal point**!

forty-six and eight tenths

tens	ones	tenths
___	___ .	___

___

twelve and three tenths

tens	ones	tenths
___	___ .	___

___

seventy-nine and one tenth

tens	ones	tenths
___	___ .	___

___

sixty-two and four tenths

tens	ones	tenths
___	___ .	___

___

Math Skill: Exploring fractions, decimals, and place-value charts

MATH

Do Decimals Make You Feel a Little TENTHS?

Shade parts of each picture to show the fraction and decimal.

$\frac{1}{10}$ = 0.1

$\frac{1}{2}$ = $\frac{5}{10}$ = 0.5

$\frac{1}{5}$ = $\frac{2}{10}$ = 0.2

Write each **fraction** as a **decimal**. Say it out loud.

$\frac{5}{10}$ _____

$\frac{3}{10}$ _____

$\frac{4}{10}$ _____

$\frac{8}{10}$ _____

Write each **decimal** as a **fraction**. Say it out loud.

0.2 _____

0.9 _____

0.3 _____

0.7 _____

Look at the pictures. Write the **fraction** and the **decimal** that tells what the picture shows. The first one is done for you.

$1\frac{6}{10}$ = 1.6

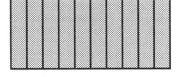
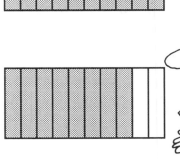

_____

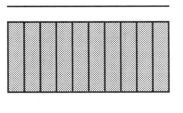
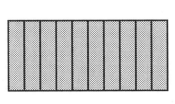

_____

Math Skill: Exploring decimals

MATH

A Decimal Dilemma

Zigga is ready to scream! She needs to do some addition. But the numbers have decimals! "That decimal point (.) keeps getting in my way!" she shouts. Read the directions, then help Zigga do a few more problems.

Add the tenths: $\begin{array}{r} 1.3 \\ +2.2 \\ \hline 5 \end{array}$	Drop down the decimal point: $\begin{array}{r} 1.3 \\ +2.2 \\ \hline .5 \end{array}$	Add the ones: $\begin{array}{r} 1.3 \\ +2.2 \\ \hline 3.5 \end{array}$

$$\begin{array}{r} 4.7 \\ +2.2 \\ \hline \end{array} \qquad \begin{array}{r} 5.2 \\ +0.6 \\ \hline \end{array} \qquad \begin{array}{r} 7.1 \\ +4.2 \\ \hline \end{array} \qquad \begin{array}{r} 6.8 \\ +10.1 \\ \hline \end{array}$$

"Arrrgh!" screams Zigga. "This problem isn't working." Look at the directions for regrouping below. Then help Zigga solve some more problems.

Add the tenths. But 14 is too big for the tenths spot! $\begin{array}{r} 3.6 \\ +4.8 \\ \hline 14 \end{array}$	Regroup the 14 into 1 one and 4 tenths. Add the one to the ones column. $\begin{array}{r} {}^{+1} \\ 3.6 \\ +4.8 \\ \hline (1)4 \end{array}$	Now drop the decimal point down. Then add the ones column! $\begin{array}{r} +1 \\ 3.6 \\ +4.8 \\ \hline 8.4 \end{array}$

$$\begin{array}{r} 5.2 \\ +2.5 \\ \hline \end{array} \quad \begin{array}{r} 7.3 \\ +7.9 \\ \hline \end{array} \quad \begin{array}{r} 2.7 \\ +3.8 \\ \hline \end{array} \quad \begin{array}{r} 13.5 \\ +\ 4.7 \\ \hline \end{array} \quad \begin{array}{r} 43.6 \\ +22.6 \\ \hline \end{array}$$

$$\begin{array}{r} 72.8 \\ +79.5 \\ \hline \end{array} \quad \begin{array}{r} 100.8 \\ +\ 19.4 \\ \hline \end{array} \quad \begin{array}{r} 98.6 \\ +98.6 \\ \hline \end{array} \quad \begin{array}{r} 125.25 \\ +180.90 \\ \hline \end{array} \quad \begin{array}{r} 460.6 \\ +352.9 \\ \hline \end{array}$$

Math Skill: Adding decimals with regrouping

MATH

Double Trouble Decimals

Can you figure out how to subtract with decimals? Tamisha knows. Watch what she does. Then try some on your own.

Subtract the tenths:	$\begin{array}{r} 7.8 \\ -3.2 \\ \hline 6 \end{array}$	Drop down the decimal point:	$\begin{array}{r} 7.8 \\ -3.2 \\ \hline .6 \end{array}$	Subtract the ones:	$\begin{array}{r} 7.8 \\ -3.2 \\ \hline 4.6 \end{array}$

$\begin{array}{r} 4.9 \\ -2.7 \\ \hline \end{array}$ $\begin{array}{r} 6.6 \\ -4.3 \\ \hline \end{array}$ $\begin{array}{r} 5.8 \\ -1.8 \\ \hline \end{array}$ $\begin{array}{r} 2.7 \\ -0.6 \\ \hline \end{array}$ $\begin{array}{r} 6.2 \\ -6.1 \\ \hline \end{array}$

Tamisha must be a genius. Watch how she subtracts this tough problem using regrouping. Then try some problems yourself, you genius you!

Subtract the tenths. But 8 is bigger than 6! Borrow a one from the 9 and regroup. $\begin{array}{r} \overset{8\ 16}{9.6} \\ -3.8 \\ \hline \end{array}$	Now you can subtract 16 − 8 in the tenths column. $\begin{array}{r} \overset{8\ 16}{9.6} \\ -3.8 \\ \hline 8 \end{array}$	Now drop down the decimal point. Last, subtract 8-3 in the ones column! $\begin{array}{r} \overset{8\ 16}{9.6} \\ -3.8 \\ \hline 5.8 \end{array}$

$\begin{array}{r} 8.7 \\ -3.9 \\ \hline \end{array}$ $\begin{array}{r} 6.3 \\ -1.8 \\ \hline \end{array}$ $\begin{array}{r} 3.8 \\ -2.9 \\ \hline \end{array}$ $\begin{array}{r} 1.2 \\ -0.4 \\ \hline \end{array}$ $\begin{array}{r} 5.5 \\ -4.8 \\ \hline \end{array}$

$\begin{array}{r} 79.5 \\ -72.8 \\ \hline \end{array}$ $\begin{array}{r} 22.7 \\ -\ 6.8 \\ \hline \end{array}$ $\begin{array}{r} 10.6 \\ -\ 3.9 \\ \hline \end{array}$ $\begin{array}{r} 188.1 \\ -\ 94.4 \\ \hline \end{array}$ $\begin{array}{r} 324.5 \\ -131.8 \\ \hline \end{array}$

How about this? Dave wanted to see how far he could go on his bike. One day, he traveled 0.7 of a mile. The next day, he went 0.4 of a mile in the morning and and 0.5 of a mile in the afternoon. How far did Dave go all together on the second day? How much further did he go on the second day than on the first day?

Math Skill: Subtracting decimals with regrouping

MATH

Like Money in Your Pocket

Look at the money in the purse. Then draw a picture of coins and dollar bills for each money amount listed below. Don't forget, there are many ways to show one amount. Ask your mom, dad, or another grown-up to count the money you drew. They'll tell you if you got it right!

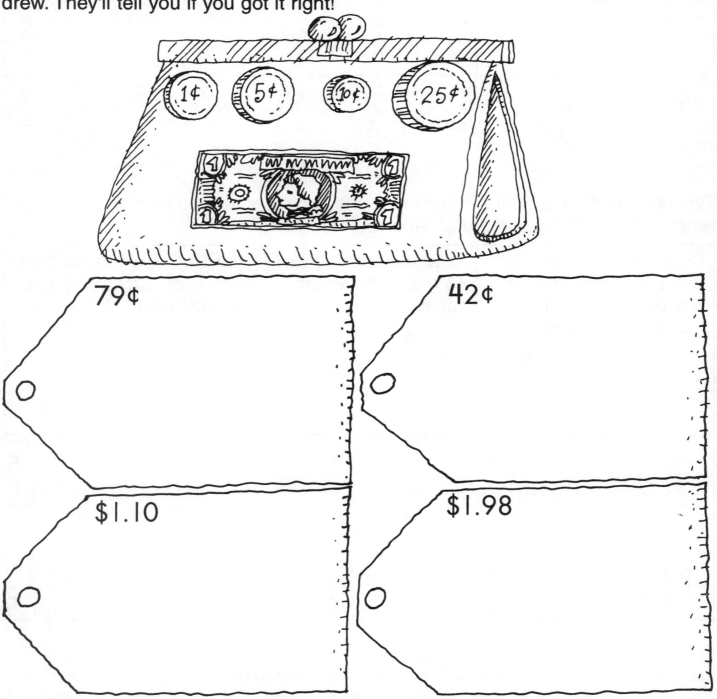

79¢

42¢

$1.10

$1.98

How about this? *Right now, do you have money in your pocket, in a drawer, or some other place? How much is it? Write the number somewhere on this page.*

Math Skill: Counting money

MATH

Count Your Change!

Toodles Frumpkin has $5.00. She spends $1.19. How much does she have left? Regrouping can tell you.

Step 1		Step 2	
Remember, you can think of $5.00 as 500 cents! Go to the hundreds column. Regroup 1 hundred as 10 tens.	$\begin{array}{r} {}^{4\ 10} \\ \$5.00 \\ -1.19 \\ \hline \end{array}$	Regroup 1 ten as 10 ones. Then subtract.	$\begin{array}{r} {}^{4\ 10\ 10}_{\ \ 9} \\ \$5.00 \\ -1.19 \\ \hline \$3.81 \end{array}$

Now you try it. Complete the subtraction problems.

$\begin{array}{r} \$5.00 \\ -1.29 \\ \hline \end{array}$
$\qquad$
$\begin{array}{r} \$3.00 \\ -1.55 \\ \hline \end{array}$

$\begin{array}{r} \$7.00 \\ -4.50 \\ \hline \end{array}$
$\qquad$
$\begin{array}{r} \$9.00 \\ -8.95 \\ \hline \end{array}$

$\begin{array}{r} \$3.99 \\ -2.75 \\ \hline \end{array}$
$\qquad$
$\begin{array}{r} \$5.65 \\ -1.82 \\ \hline \end{array}$

$\begin{array}{r} \$2.34 \\ -\ .50 \\ \hline \end{array}$
$\qquad$
$\begin{array}{r} \$6.25 \\ -5.45 \\ \hline \end{array}$

Math Skill: Subtracting money

MATH

A Good Deal

Gerd and Lerd are going berzerk at the mall! They want special matching hats. Lerd buys the hat in the first store he sees it. He doesn't know that another store might sell it to him for less money! Gerd sees the same hat in two different stores. She asks how much it is. Gerd buys the hat in the store with the lower price.

Write a number to show how much Gerd saves by not shopping where Lerd shops.

Lerd: 75¢
Gerd: 56¢

Savings: _____

Lerd: 98¢
Gerd: 50¢

Savings: _____

Lerd: 42¢
Gerd: 17¢

Savings: _____

Lerd: $1.19
Gerd: 89¢

Savings: _____

Lerd: $2.50
Gerd: $1.39

Savings: _____

Lerd: $3.14
Gerd: $2.89

Savings: _____

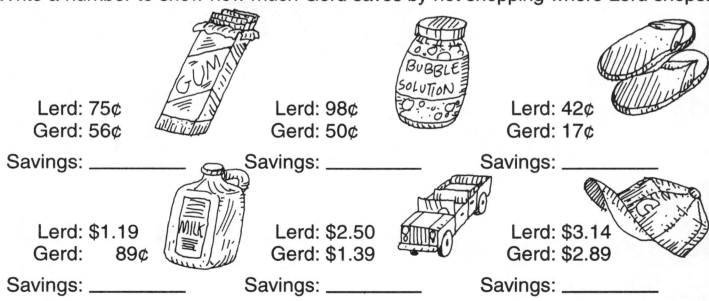

How about this? *Compare the prices of two items in two different stores. You might try milk and some kind of fruit.*

Math Skill: Comparing money amounts

MATH

A Shopping List

Here's nine dollars. How many things could you buy with it? Get real prices, in a food store, toy store, or a mall. Try to get as much as you can for $9.00.

Item	Price
_____	_____
_____	_____
_____	_____
_____	_____
_____	_____
_____	_____
_____	_____
_____	_____
_____	_____
_____	_____
_____	_____
_____	_____

Total amount spent: _____

Change left over from $9.00: _____

Math Skill: Solving real-world money problems

MATH

Big Bucks

Suppose you had one hundred, two hundred, three hundred or more dollars. What if you spent some? How would you know how much you had left? Jeb decided to count it all. He'll be here all day! It would be faster to subtract on paper. Give it a try!

Now you try it. Remember to regroup.

$300.00	$400.00	$800.00	$625.00	$976.00
−142.00	−168.00	−267.00	−214.00	−782.00

	$742.00	$300.00	$551.75	$243.65
	−357.00	−163.25	−340.80	−175.28

Math Skill: Subtracting money with regrouping

MATH

Bargain Busters

The shopping club had a contest at the mall. Who got the best deals? Look at each item they bought. Circle the name of the kid who paid the lower price for it. Then subtract to find out the difference in the prices. Write the answer on the line.

Pam	$31.00
Bam	$24.00

_____

Dick	$15.05
Doc	12.95

_____

Mollie	$110.95
Paulie	$98.20

_____

Sam	$204.57
Tam	$178.43

_____

How about this? _Get a catalog or a sale ad from a newspaper. Make a list of the things you would like to buy. Add up the prices to find the total cost._

Math Skill: Adding and subtracting money amounts

MATH

It's About Time

Look at the clock. The short hand is the hour hand. It points to the hour. The long hand is the minute hand. It points to the minute.

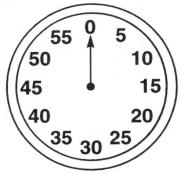

You can count by ones to read the hour.

You can count by fives to read the minutes.

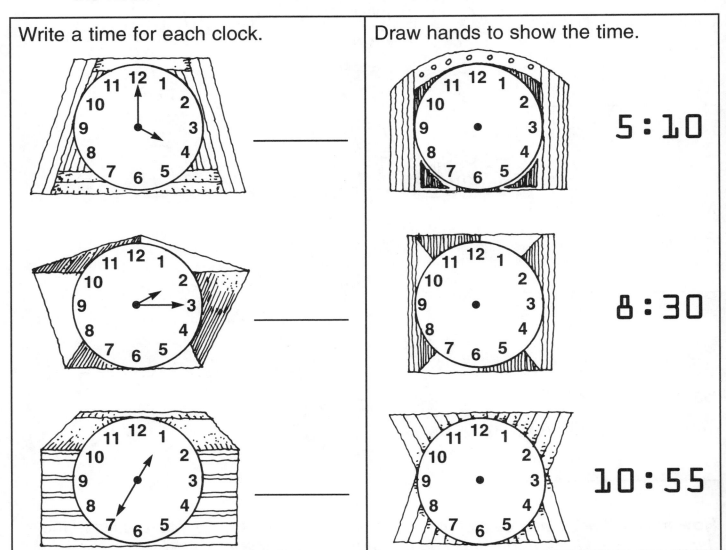

Write a time for each clock.

Draw hands to show the time.

_____

_____

_____

5:10

8:30

10:55

Math Skill: Reading analog clocks

MATH

Time After Time

Digitial clocks don't have big hands or little hands. But they are still a good way to tell the time! Can you match the clocks that tell the same times? Draw a line to connect them.

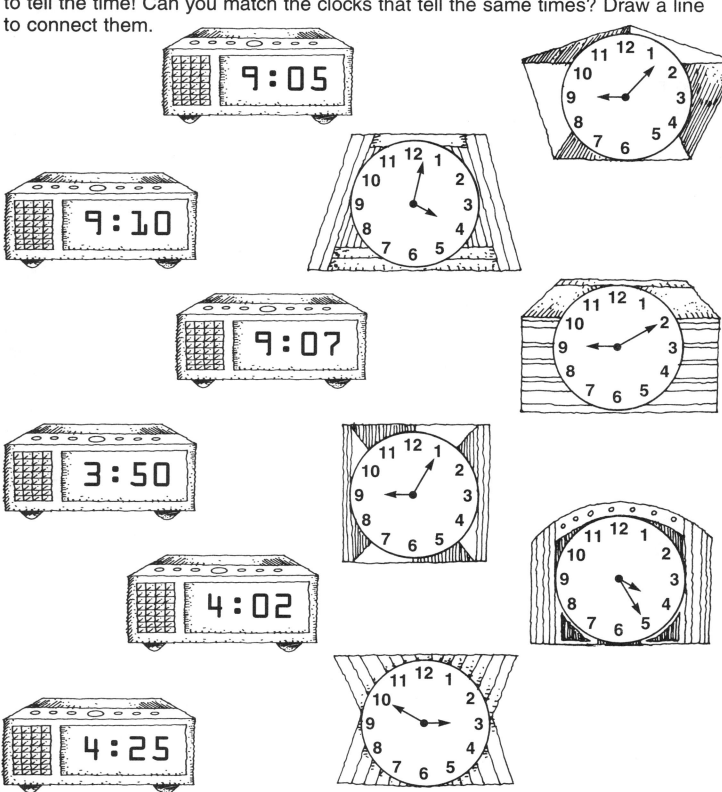

Math Skill: Telling time with analog and digital clocks

MATH

Time Flies

Here is a schedule of what Gerald did today.

4:00 Boarded the bus for the mall
4:30 Arrived at the mall
4:35 Walked around looking for his friend Ginger
5:00 Found Ginger buying posters for her room
5:30 Left the mall with Ginger
6:05 Arrived at Ginger's house and played video games
6:30 Ate lunch with Ginger's mom
8:00 Got into Ginger's mom's car
8:35 Got home

Draw hands on the clocks to show the time.

Gerald got on the bus.

Gerald arrived at the mall.

Gerald and Ginger arrived at Ginger's house.

Gerald got into Ginger's mom's car.

How many minutes did Gerald spend on the bus? _____

How many minutes did it take Gerald to find Ginger? _____

How long was Gerald's car ride home? _____

How about this? *Make your own schedule! Write the number of minutes it takes you to get up, dress for school, get to school, do your homework, eat dinner, brush your teeth, and read a page of your favorite book.*

Math Skill: Exploring elapsed time

MATH

How Big Is an Inch?

An inch is used to measure length. An inch is always the same length. You can use a ruler to measure one half (½) of an inch and one fourth (¼) of an inch.

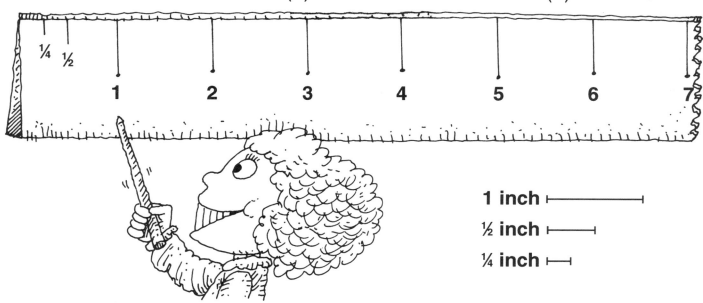

There are lots of things you can measure. Start by estimating the number of inches each thing is. Write the number in the chart. Then measure it using the ruler above. Write the actual answer in the chart. Write in some of your own measurement challenges, too!

Object	Estimate	Actual Length
length of your little finger		
width of your little finger		
width of one hand		
thickness of a book		
length of one strand of your hair		
length of your foot		

Math Skill: Measuring to the nearest inch

MATH

Inch, Foot, and Yard

There are 12 inches in one foot. A ruler is one foot long. There are 3 feet in one yard. A yardstick is is one yard long. Write **inch**, **foot**, or **yard** to tell what you would use to measure each of these things.

your finger   _____

your hand   _____

your foot   _____

your height   _____

the height of a parent   _____

the length of a long table   _____

one sticker   _____

a crayon box   _____

length of cloth for a ghost costume _____

the width of a room   _____

Math Skill: Differentiating between an inch, foot, and yard

126

MATH

How Do You Measure Up?
To make Muckity-Muck Soup, measure out all of your ingredients carefully.

2 cups = 1 pint	2 pints = 1 quart

2 quarts = 1 half-gallon	**2 half-gallons = 1 gallon**
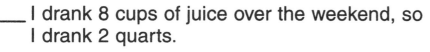	

Read these sentences about liquids you can measure. Some of the sentences are false! Draw pictures to help you figure out which ones aren't true. Put an **X** next to those sentences.

___ Two people with a half-gallon of juice can each drink 2 quarts.	
___ I drank 8 cups of juice over the weekend, so I drank 2 quarts.	
___ I spilled 8 half-gallons of milk on the floor. That means I'm standing in a 3-gallon puddle!	

How about this? *You and a friend can measure water with old milk cartons. Ask each other some tough questions. For example, which is greater: 4 pints or 3 quarts?*

Math Skill: Measuring liquid capacity

MATH

Pick a Pictograph

Many kids in Mr. Tilly's third grade class have collections. Some collect finger puppets. Others collect fuzzy pencils. Mr. Tilly made two pictographs about the kids' collections. Read the key for each pictograph. Then answer the questions at the bottom.

Number of Finger Puppets in a Collection

Justin	●●●●●
Sarah	●●●
Tim	●●
Emily	●●●●●●

Key: Each ● stands for 2 finger puppets.

Number of Fuzzy Pencils in a Collection

Samantha	●●●
Joseph	●●●●●●●●
Michael	●●●●●●
Jennifer	●●●●●●●●●●●●●●
Jessica	●●●●●●●

Key: Each ● stands for 5 fuzzy pencils.

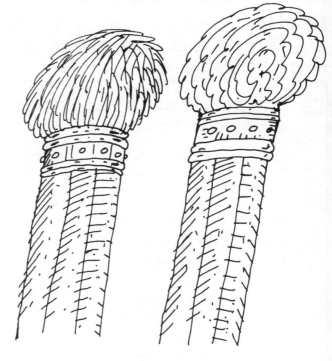

Who has the most finger puppets? _____

How many does that person have? _____

Who has the smallest amount of fuzzy pencils? _____

Who has the greatest amount of fuzzy pencils? _____

How many more does that person have? _____

Math Skill: Reading a pictograph

Ashley

Don't Laugh at Graphs

Every week, Jody takes a spelling test of 10 words. Spelling really gives her a lot of trouble. Jody decided to make a graph to show the number of words she gets right over 10 weeks. Look what happened the first 2 weeks.

	1	2	3	4	5	6	7	8	9	10
Week 1	▓	▓	▓							
Week 2	▓	▓	▓	▓	▓	▓				
Week 3										
Week 4										
Week 5										
Week 6										
Week 7										
Week 8										
Week 9										
Week 10										

How many words did Jody get right in week 1? _____

How many words did Jody get right in week 2? _____

Now fill in the bars for the other weeks.

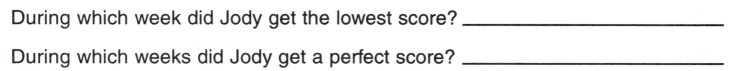

- **Week 3**: Jody has 4 correct spelling words.
- **Week 4**: Jody has 7 correct spelling words.
- **Week 5**: Jody has 10 correct spelling words.
- **Week 6**: Jody has 2 correct spelling words.
- **Week 7**: Jody has 9 correct spelling words.
- **Week 8**: Jody has 10 correct spelling words.
- **Week 9**: Jody has 8 correct spelling words.
- **Week 10**: Jody has 10 correct spelling words.

During which week did Jody get the lowest score? _____

During which weeks did Jody get a perfect score? _____

Math Skill: Completing and interpreting a bar graph

MATH

Taking a Survey

Ask family, friends, and neighbors to look at the list below. Then ask them which activity on the list is their favorite. Make a tally mark next to their answer.

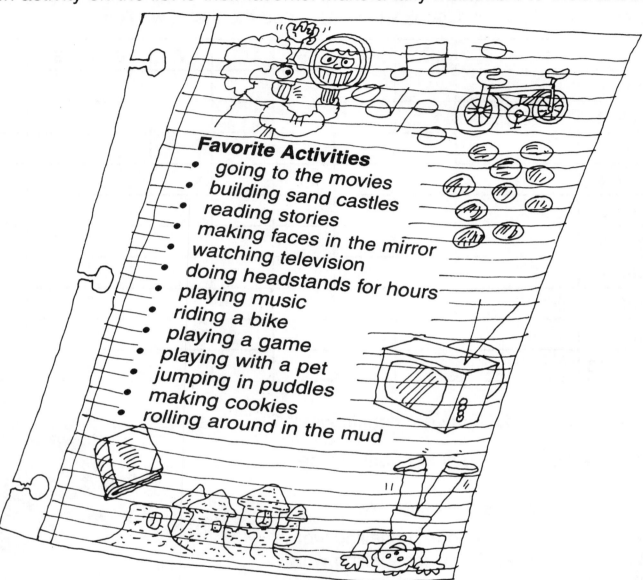

Think about what the people in your survey said.

Which was the favorite activity? _____

How many people chose it? _____

How many chose the second most popular activity? _____

How many activities were chosen by just one person? _____

Math Skill: Making a tally table

MATH

A Map of Feartown

You'd better not set foot in Feartown unless you know where you're going! You can use a **grid map**. Numbers on the grid can tell you where things are on the map. These numbers are called **ordered pairs**. Boneyard Hollow can be found at the **ordered pair 3, 5**. How do you get there?

- Start at 0.
- Go across to 3.
- Go up to 5.
- Boneyard Hollow is located at (3, 5).

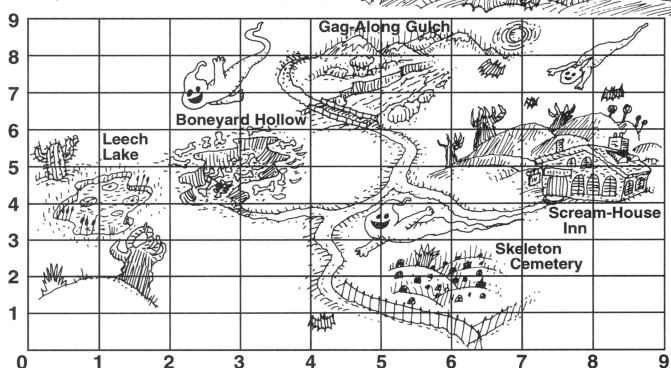

Write the ordered sets that tell where you can find these other horrible places!

Leech Lake _____   Skeleton Cemetery _____

Gag-Along Gulch _____   Scream-House Inn _____

Where would you build your very own haunted house in Feartown? Draw it in a vacant lot. Then write down a name for it below, along with the ordered pair that tells where it is. Then do the same for a ghoul-school!

- Your haunted house: _____ at ordered pair _____ .

- Your scary school: _____ at ordered pair _____ .

Math Skill: Using ordered pairs

MATH MASTER'S PUZZLE BOOK

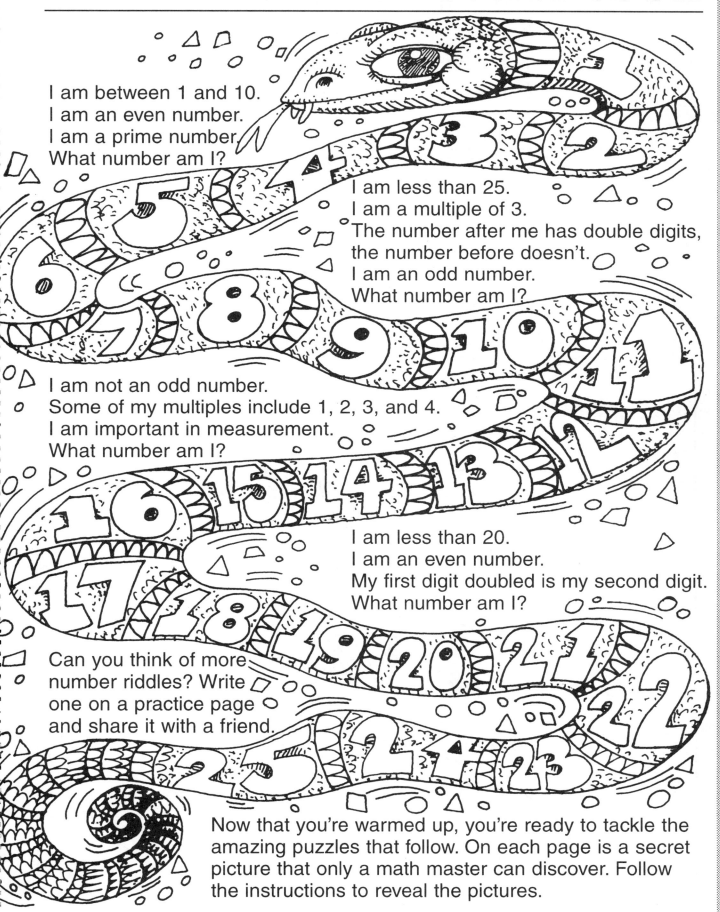

I am between 1 and 10.
I am an even number.
I am a prime number.
What number am I?

I am less than 25.
I am a multiple of 3.
The number after me has double digits,
the number before doesn't.
I am an odd number.
What number am I?

I am not an odd number.
Some of my multiples include 1, 2, 3, and 4.
I am important in measurement.
What number am I?

I am less than 20.
I am an even number.
My first digit doubled is my second digit.
What number am I?

Can you think of more
number riddles? Write
one on a practice page
and share it with a friend.

Now that you're warmed up, you're ready to tackle the
amazing puzzles that follow. On each page is a secret
picture that only a math master can discover. Follow
the instructions to reveal the pictures.

Color in each space that shows the answer to an addition problem on this page. Answers may appear more than once.

2 + 20 =   5 + 5 =   9 + 9 =   6 + 6 =
3 + 24 =   7 + 7 =   4 + 22 =   8 + 8 =
9 + 8 =   5 + 4 =   33 + 4 =   22 + 3 =
7 + 6 =   8 + 7 =   2 + 1 =   6 + 5 =

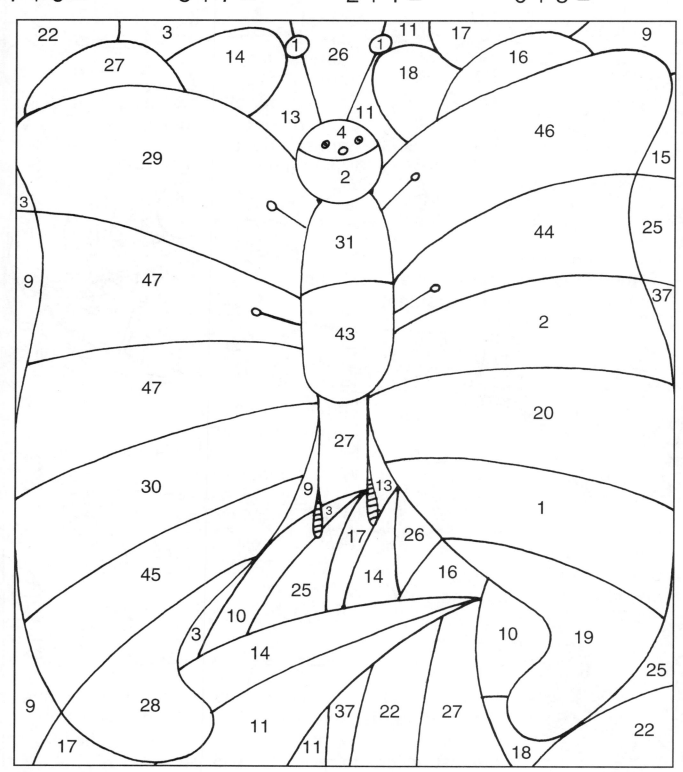

Color in each space that shows the
answer to an addition problem on this page.

$2 + 2 + 4 =$ $5 + 3 + 4 =$ $1 + 9 + 4 =$ $2 + 6 + 2 =$

$5 + 6 + 0 =$ $4 + 2 + 3 =$ $7 + 6 + 5 =$ $1 + 12 + 3 =$

$13 + 6 + 1 =$ $8 + 7 + 4 =$ $0 + 3 + 2 =$ $6 + 5 + 6 =$

$3 + 6 + 6 =$ $3 + 7 + 3 =$ $4 + 1 + 2 =$ $1 + 2 + 3 =$

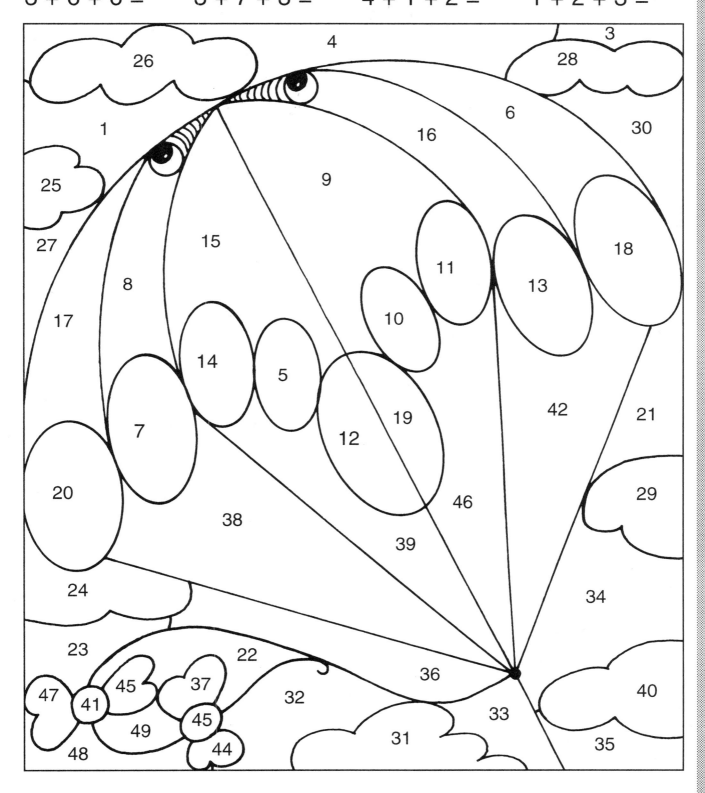

Color in each space that shows the answer to a subtraction problem on this page. Answers may appear more than once.

10 − 2 =   5 − 3 =   9 − 6 =   8 − 2 =

7 − 3 =   8 − 7 =   12 − 3 =   8 − 1 =

19 − 7 =   20 − 4 =   11 − 6 =   18 − 5 =

20 − 6 =   17 − 6 =   19 − 4 =   16 − 6 =

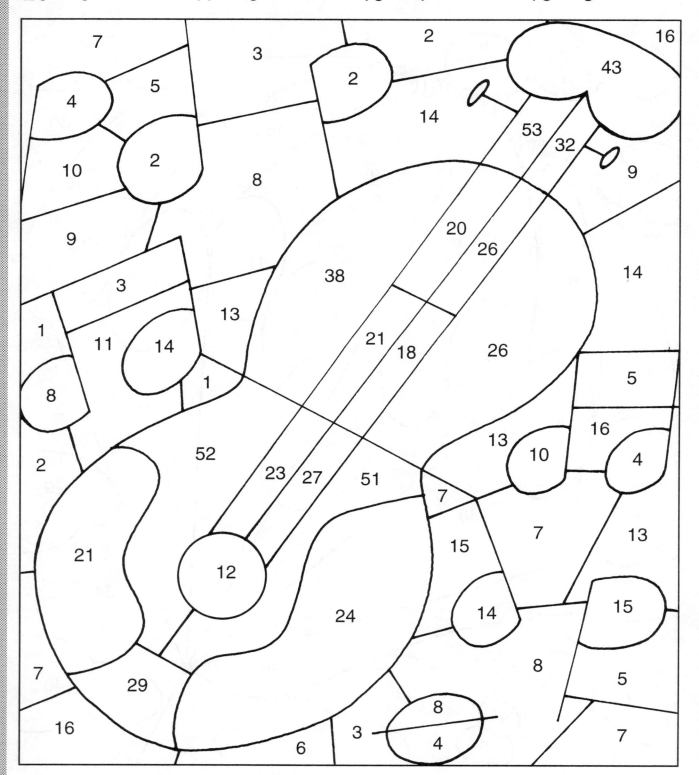

1. Circle the correct symbol in each equation.
2. Find the difference.
3. Color in each space that shows the difference from an equation on this page. If > was circled, color the space yellow. If < was circled, color it pink.

2 < or > 4   15 < or > 19   20 < or > 17   12 < or > 18

1 < or > 14   19 < or > 3   4 < or > 19   18 < or > 4

20 < or > 15   17 < or > 16   8 < or > 15   12 < or > 2

16 < or > 7   9 < or > 17   20 < or > 8   8 < or > 19

Fill in the blanks as you skip count by 2's.
Then color in each space in the picture that has one of those numbers.

2 ___ 6 ___ ___ 12 ___ ___ ___ 20 ___ ___ ___ ___

___ 32 ___ ___ ___ ___ ___ 44 ___ ___ ___ ___ 52 ___

___ ___ 60 ___ ___ ___ ___ ___ ___ ___ ___ 76 ___ ___

___ ___ ___ 88 ___ ___ ___ ___ ___ 100

Fill in the blanks as you skip count by 5's.
Then color in each space in the box that has one of those numbers.

5 ___ ___ ___ ___ ___ ___ ___ 45 ___ ___ ___ ___

___ 75 ___ ___ ___ ___ ___

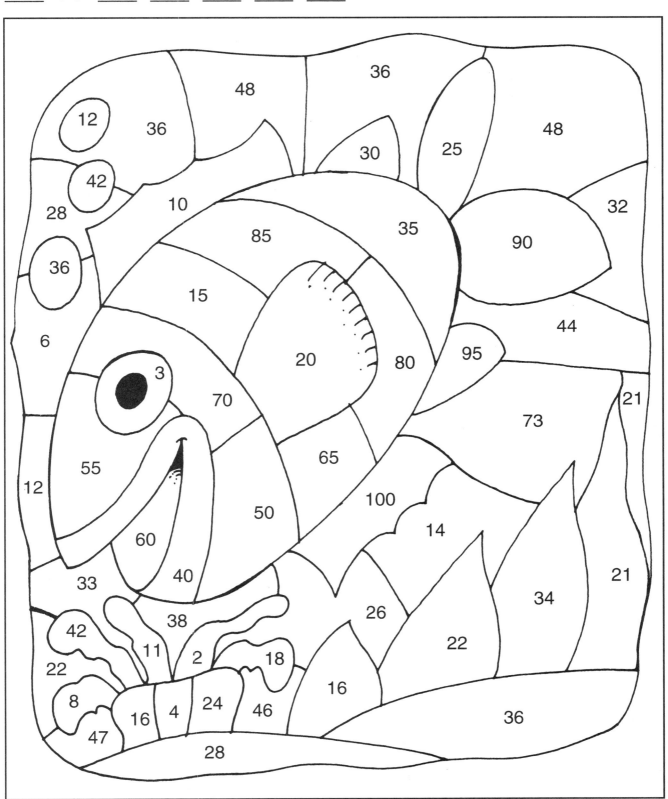

Fill in the blanks as you skip count by 10's.
Then color in each space that has one of those numbers in the box.

10 ___ ___ ___ ___ 60 ___ ___ ___ ___ 110 ___ ___

140 ___ ___ ___ ___ 190 ___

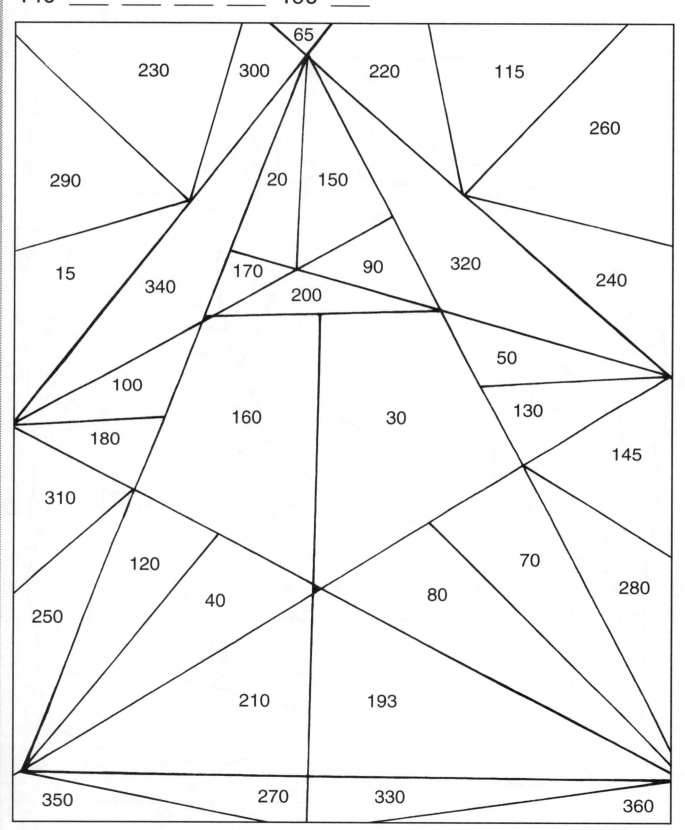

Find the correct math symbol (+, −, x, ÷) for each problem.
Then find each answer number in the box below.
If it's the answer to an addition problem, color the space blue.
If it's the answer to a subtraction problem, color the space red.
If it's the answer to a multiplication problem, color the space green.
If it's the answer to a division problem, color the space brown.

4 ◯ 6 = 24   5 ◯ 3 = 8   22 ◯ 2 = 44   28 ◯ 8 = 36

24 ◯ 4 = 6   7 ◯ 6 = 42   9 ◯ 7 = 2   8 ◯ 8 = 64

22 ◯ 2 = 20   25 ◯ 5 = 30   4 ◯ 6 = 10   11 ◯ 2 = 9

5 ◯ 1 = 5   7 ◯ 4 = 11   18 ◯ 18 = 0   15 ◯ 5 = 3

33 ◯ 7 = 26   45 ◯ 14 = 31   35 ◯ 1 = 35   80 ◯ 2 = 40

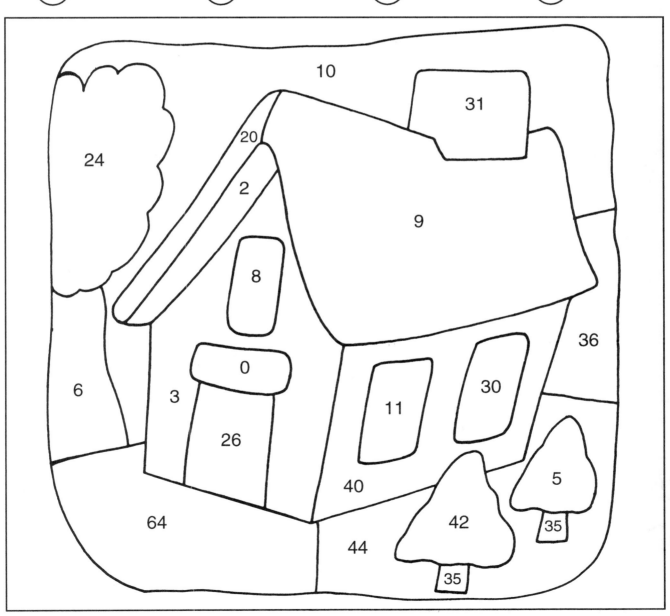

Color each space that has an even number over 50 purple.
Color each space that has an odd number over 50 green.

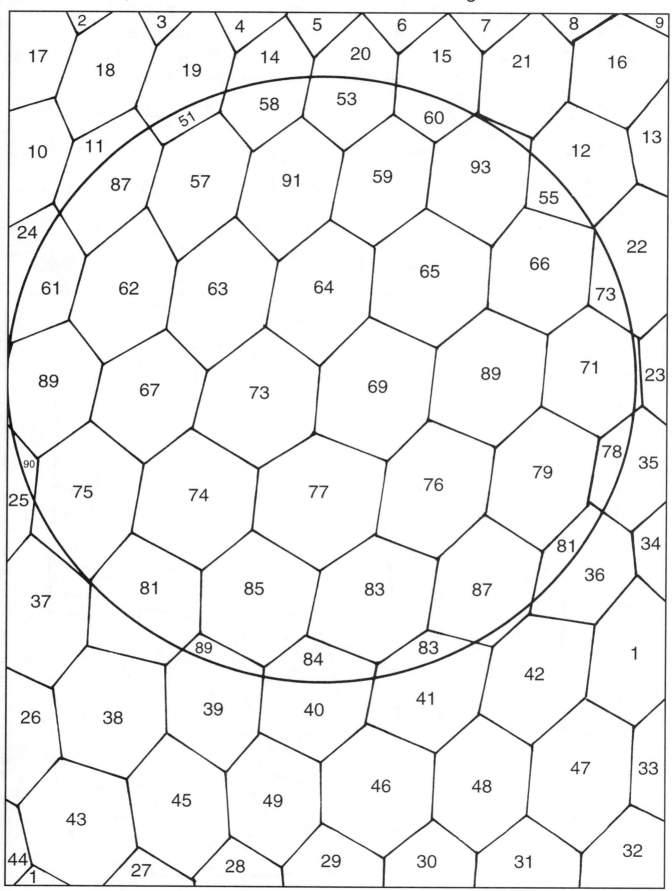

Look at the blocks below. Write in the numbers they show. Then color in the spaces that show those numbers. If the number is in the tens, color the space red. If it is in the hundreds, color it blue. If it is in the thousands, color it yellow. Answers may appear more than once.

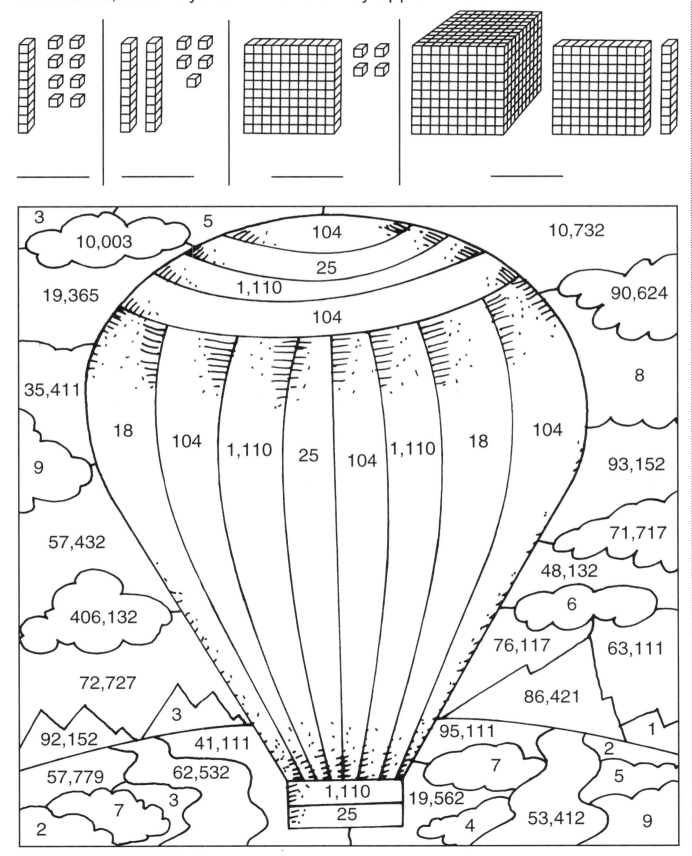

Color each space that has a number in the **thousands** green. Color each space that has a number in the **ten thousands** brown. Color each space that has a number in the **hundred thousands** orange.

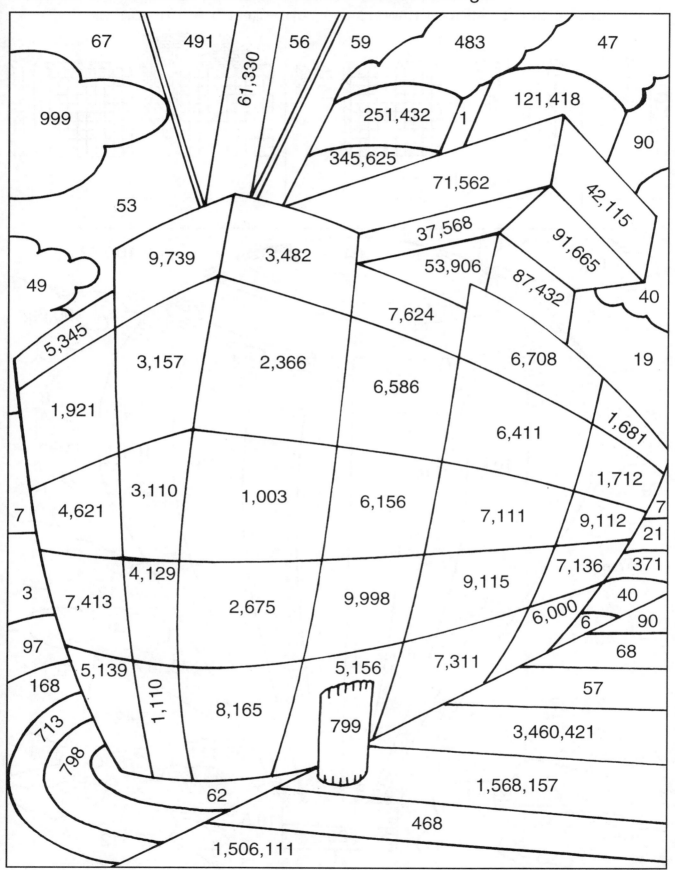

Color in each space that shows the answer to a multiplication problem on this page. Answers may appear more than once.

2 x 5 =   3 x 6 =   8 x 4 =   5 x 3 =

2 x 6 =   7 x 2 =   3 x 7 =   4 x 6 =

5 x 6 =   9 x 3 =   7 x 4 =   5 x 8 =

5 x 9 =   2 x 8 =   5 x 4 =   4 x 9 =

Color in each space that shows the answer to an addition problem on this page. Answers may appear more than once.

24	38	62	44	19	53
+62	+51	+37	+44	+50	+24
——	——	——	——	——	——

71	84	28	46	60	54
+13	+12	+30	+52	+22	+20
——	——	——	——	——	——

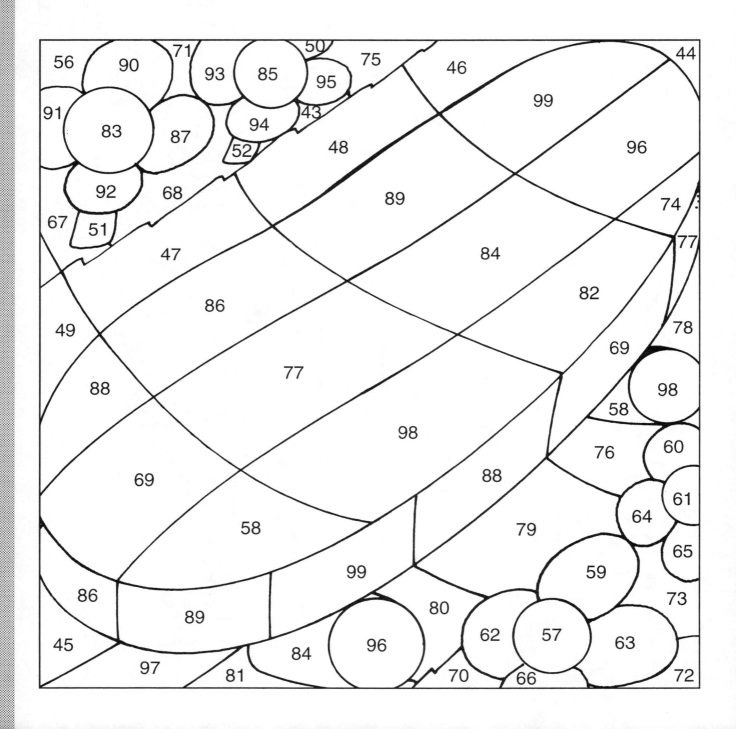

Color in each space that shows the answer to an addition problem on this page. Answers may appear more than once.

27	73	36	54	49	65
+45	+17	+38	+39	+25	+27

49	65	73	48	42	36
+23	+27	+18	+12	+39	+54

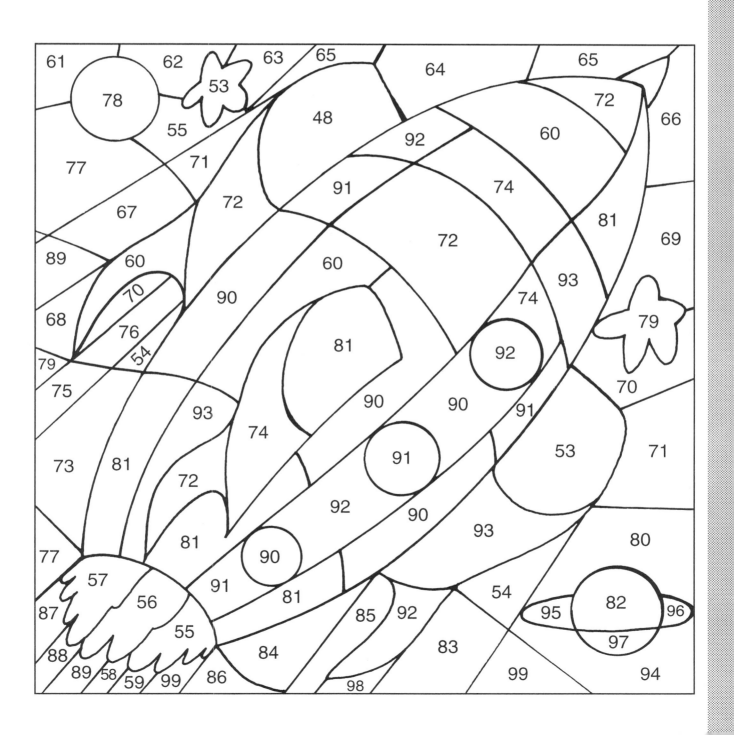

Color in each space that shows the answer to a subtraction problem on this page. Answers may appear more than once.

49	38	96	17	59	75
-26	-14	-63	-11	-30	-24

98	82	23	64	60	51
-83	-52	-12	-42	-20	-30

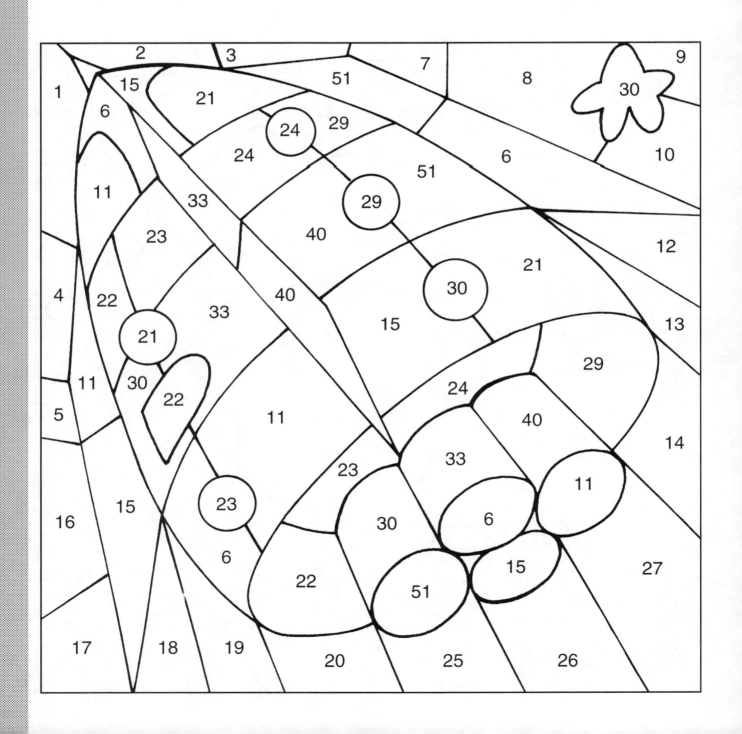

Color in each space that shows the answer to a subtraction problem on this page. Answers may appear more than once.

58	82	63	71	94	85
−29	−45	−37	−18	−36	−26

67	76	42	56	60	34
−58	−57	−14	−48	−22	−19

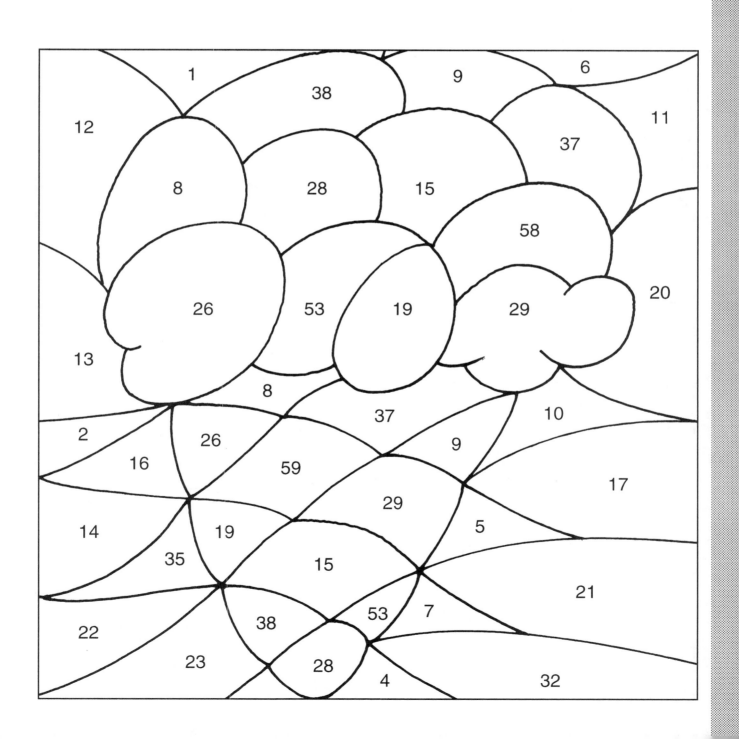

Color in each space that shows the answer to a multiplication problem on this page. Answers may appear more than once.

6 x 7 =   7 x 9 =   8 x 6 =   9 x 8 =
8 x 8 =   9 x 6 =   9 x 9 =   10 x 6 =
8 x 7 =   10 x 9 =   7 x 7 =   10 x 8 =
7 x 10 =   9 x 4 =   8 x 5 =   3 x 10 =

Color in each space that shows the answer to a multiplication problem on this page.

21 x 4 =   33 x 2 =   32 x 3 =   14 x 2 =

12 x 4 =   31 x 3 =   10 x 9 =   34 x 2 =

41 x 7 =   11 x 9 =   51 x 7 =   63 x 2 =

71 x 5 =   92 x 4 =   83 x 3 =   7 x 4 =

5 x 5 =   6 x 6 =   6 x 3 =   6 x 7 =

5 x 4 =   5 x 9 =   11 x 8 =   32 x 2 =

Color the areas that contain fractions that are equal to the diagrams below. If the fraction is greater than 1/2, color it orange. If it is less than or equal to 1/2, color it yellow.

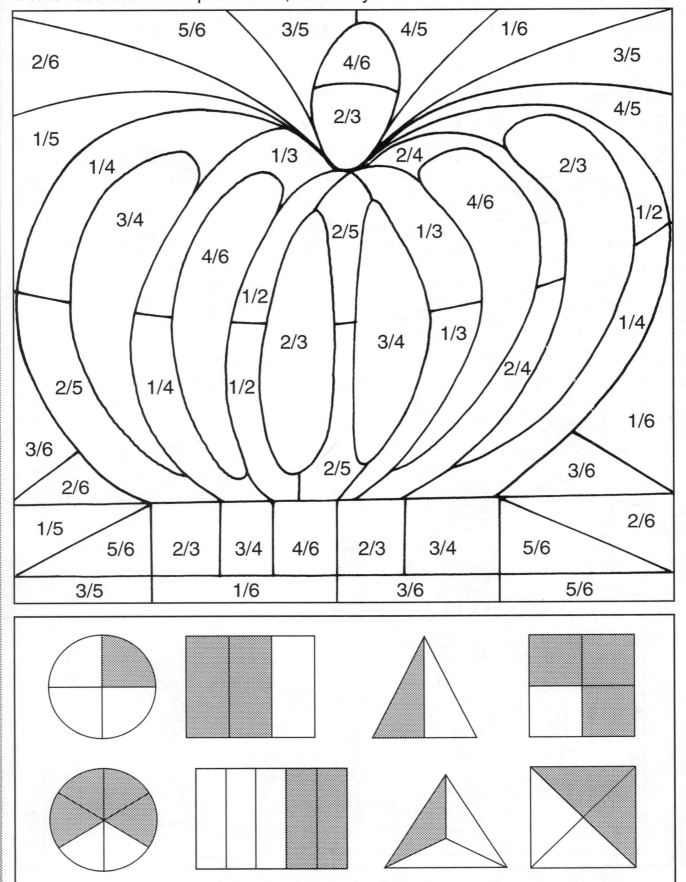

Convert each fraction to a decimal. Color the areas that contain those decimals. Decimals may appear more than once.

3/10	_____	6/10	_____
9/10	_____	2/10	_____
4/10	_____	1/10	_____
7/10	_____	5/10	_____
8/10	_____	10/10	_____

0.12　0.12　0.21

0.71

0.31　0.1　0.8　0.2

0.2　0.7　0.1　0.6　0.13

0.5　1.0

0.9

0.41　0.3　0.6　1.0　0.4　0.8　0.61

0.4　0.5　0.9　0.3　0.7　0.21

0.21　0.1　0.31

0.91　0.4　0.11　0.71　1.0　0.21

0.1　0.71　0.1　0.9　0.41

0.11　0.5　0.17

0.71　0.6　0.41　0.2　0.81　0.5　0.51

0.3　0.61

0.12　0.3　0.81　0.8　0.6　0.2

0.5

0.18　0.91　0.4

0.7

0.91　0.2　0.6　0.71

0.7　0.3　0.8

0.51　0.4　1.0　0.1　0.2

0.9　0.3　0.7　0.3　0.6　0.8

0.5

0.81　0.91　0.4　0.9　0.12　0.21　0.31　0.41　0.51　0.61

Color in each space that shows the answer to a decimal addition problem on this page. Answers may appear more than once.

8.6	7.1	4.6	1.4	3.4	5.6
+1.2	+2.5	+5.3	+7.4	+4.2	+3.1

2.2	6.7	53.4	76.5	42.7	64.2
+4.6	+1.2	+32.5	+23.2	+47.1	+25.5

Color in each space that shows the answer to a decimal subtraction problem on this page. Answers may appear more than once.

6.5	8.9	4.6	2.8	1.9	9.5
− 2.3	− 6.7	− 3.2	− 1.8	− 1.2	− 7.4

7.4	5.7	34.9	54.6	78.1	64.7
− 5.1	− 4.4	− 12.6	− 31.4	− 42.0	− 51.3

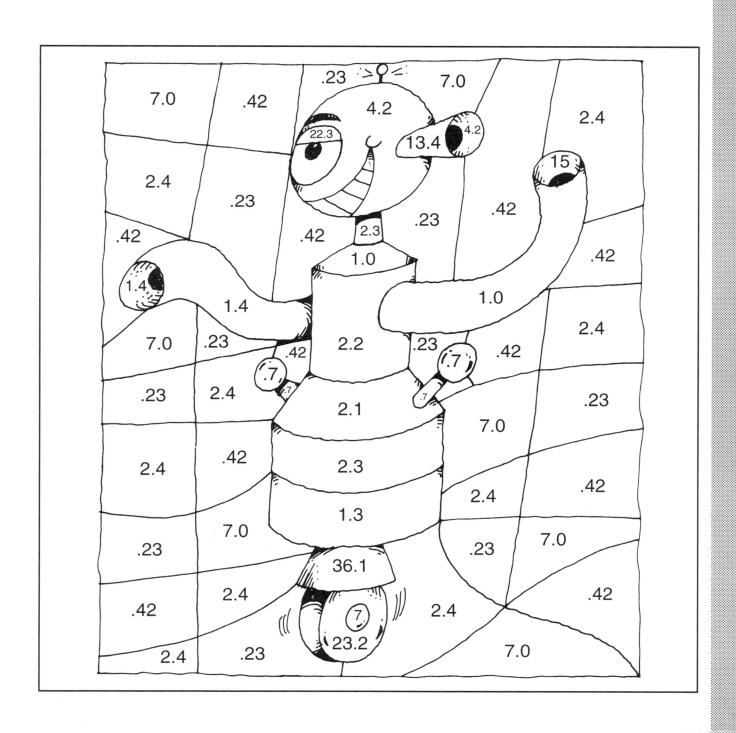

Color in each space that shows the answer to a money subtraction problem on this page. Answers may appear more than once.

$7.50	$8.98	$4.66	$9.84	$2.19	$3.95
− 2.30	− 4.25	− 2.43	− 6.82	− 1.14	− 2.41

$5.74	$6.58	$7.38	$8.54	$6.93	$5.45
− 3.52	− 4.44	− 1.26	− 3.14	− 4.20	− 1.29

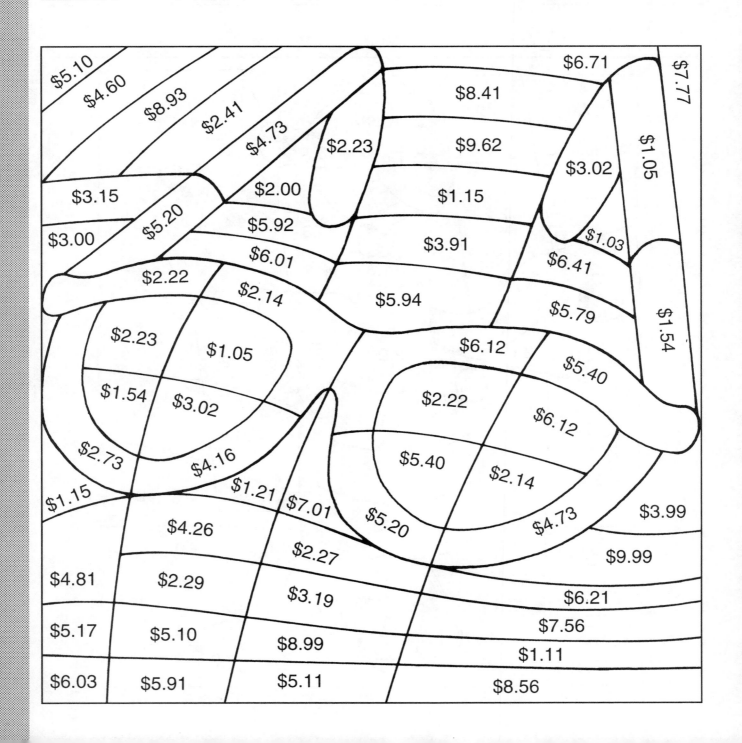

Color in each space that shows the answer to a money addition problem on this page. Answers may appear more than once.
If the answer is more than $9.00, color the space brown.
If the answer is between $7.00 and $9.00, color the space yellow.
If the answer is between $5.00 and $6.00, color the space blue.
If the answer is less than $5.00, color the space green.

$3.80	$7.65	$8.37	$5.53	$4.74
+5.14	+2.23	+1.32	+2.46	+4.24

$2.58	$8.35	$6.32	$1.53	$4.55
+3.21	+1.62	+2.25	+3.25	+2.42

$2.77	$2.25
+3.12	+2.54

$7.99

$5.90

$5.90

$8.94 $8.94 $8.94 $8.94 $8.94 $8.94 $8.94 $8.94 $8.94

$8.94

$9.69

$5.89

$5.89

$6.96

$5.89

$8.00

$4.78

$9.88

$5.79

$6.96

$9.98 $9.98

$9.97

$5.79

$9.97

$6.96 $8.98 $6.96

$7.99

$4.79

$4.79

$5.89

$9.98 $9.98

$6.96

$8.92 $9.70

$4.78

$7.99

$9.70

$8.57

$8.92

$4.78

$4.78

$8.92

$8.92

$4.79

$4.79

$4.79

$4.78

Solve each equation. Color in each space that shows another equation whose answer equals the answer to an equation on this page.

$4 \times 4 =$ $3 \times 2 =$ $8 \times 3 =$ $11 \times 2 =$

$5 \times 4 =$ $6 \times 3 =$ $5 \times 9 =$ $4 \times 2 =$

$6 + 6 =$ $10 + 4 =$ $3 + 18 =$ $5 + 20 =$

$5 + 5 =$ $15 + 15 =$ $24 + 8 =$ $18 + 18 =$

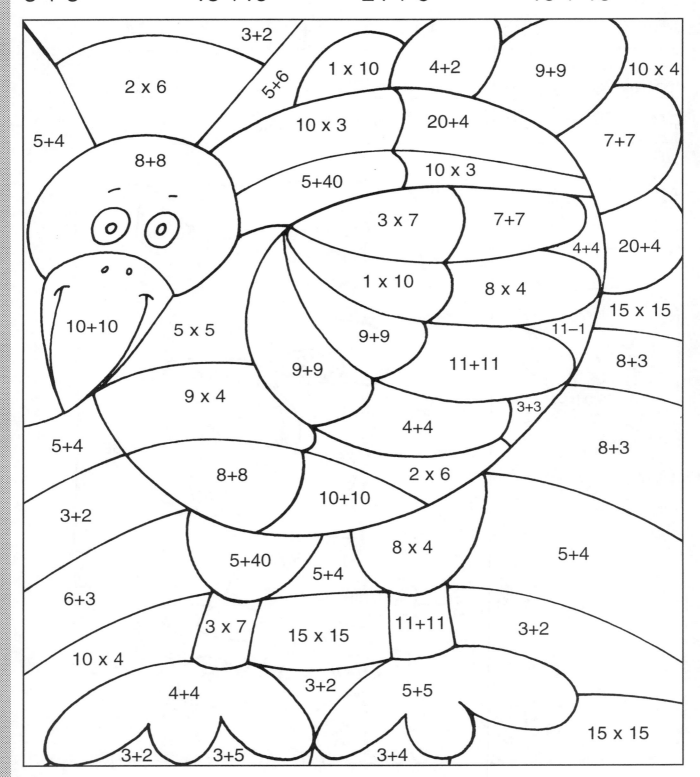

Color the areas that contain the times that are shown below.
If the time is shown on a digital clock, color the space yellow.
If it is on an analog clock, color the space green.

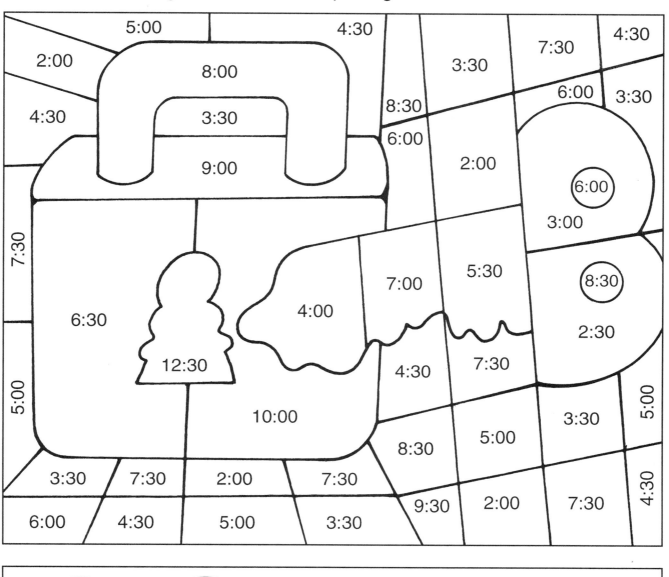

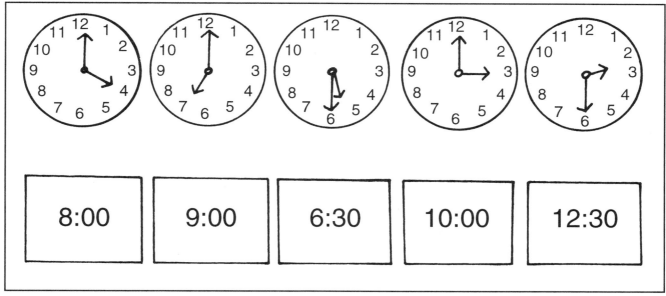

Color the areas that contain the times that are shown below.
If the time is shown on a digital clock, color the space brown.
If it is shown on an analog clock, color the space yellow.

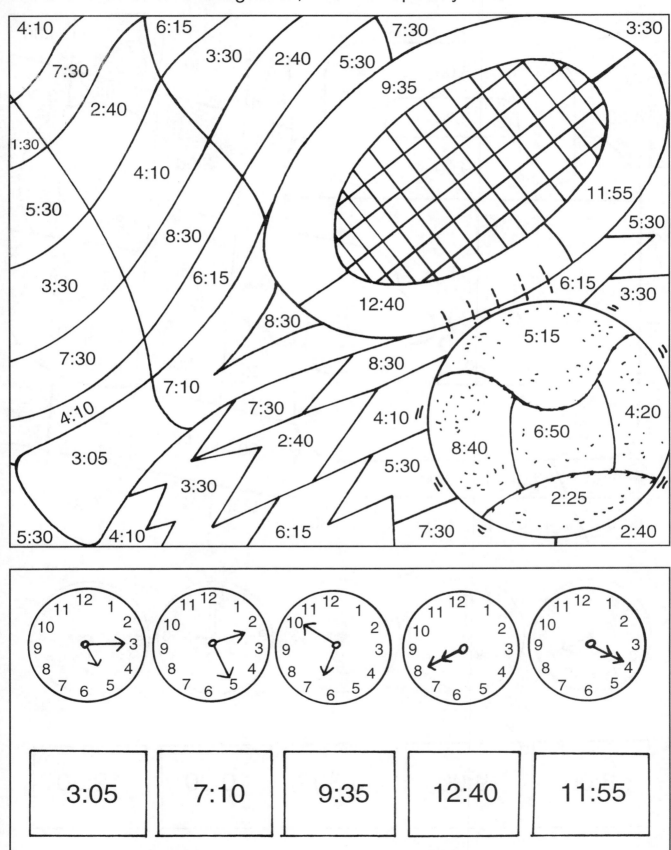

Color in each space that shows the answer to a division problem on this page.

$16 \div 4 =$ $56 \div 7 =$ $6 \div 2 =$ $35 \div 7 =$

$63 \div 9 =$ $66 \div 11 =$ $12 \div 6 =$ $18 \div 2 =$

$88 \div 8 =$ $144 \div 12=$ $80 \div 8 =$ $12 \div 12 =$

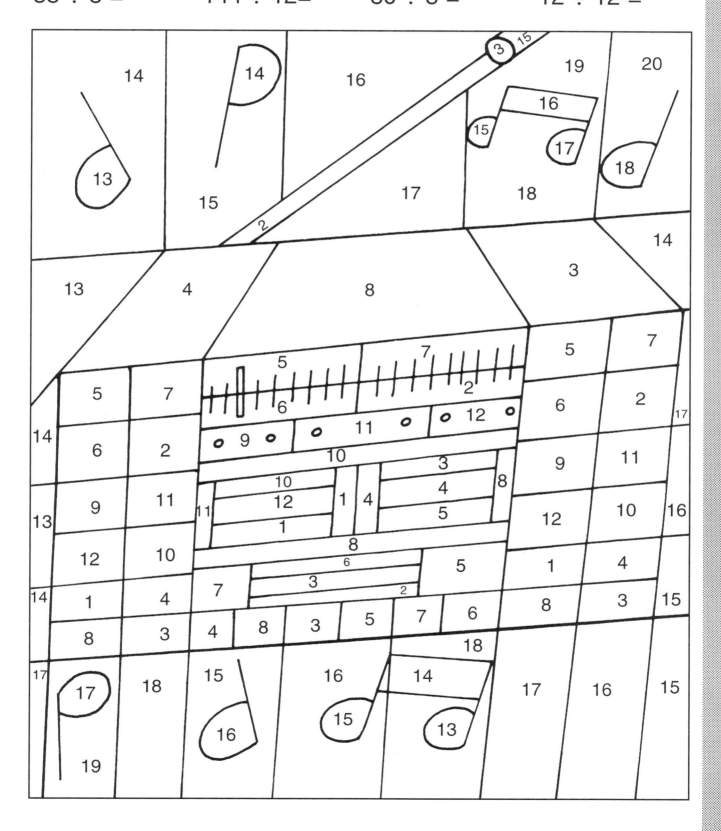

ANSWERS

Page 1 Riddles: 2; 9; 1/2; 12

P 134

2 + 20 = 22	5 + 5 = 10	9 + 9 = 18	6 + 6 = 12
3 + 24 = 27	7 + 7 = 14	4 + 22 = 26	8 + 8 = 16
9 + 8 = 17	5 + 4 = 9	33 + 4 = 37	22 + 3 = 25
7 + 6 = 13	8 + 7 = 15	2 + 1 = 3	6 + 5 = 11

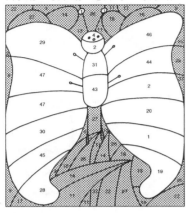

P 135

2 + 2 + 4 = 8	5 + 3 + 4 = 12	1 + 9 + 4 = 14	2 + 6 + 2 = 10
5 + 6 + 0 = 11	4 + 2 + 3 = 9	7 + 6 + 5 = 18	1 + 12 + 3 = 16
13 + 6 + 1 = 20	8 + 7 + 4 = 19	0 + 3 + 2 = 5	6 + 5 + 6 = 17
3 + 6 + 6 = 15	3 + 7 + 3 = 13	4 + 1 + 2 = 7	1 + 2 + 3 = 6

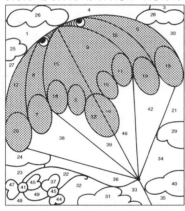

P 136

10 − 2 = 8	5 − 3 = 2	9 − 6 = 3	8 − 2 = 6
7 − 3 = 4	8 − 7 = 1	12 − 3 = 9	8 − 1 = 7
19 − 7 = 12	20 − 4 = 16	11 − 6 = 5	18 − 5 = 13
20 − 6 = 14	17 − 6 = 11	19 − 4 = 15	16 − 6 = 10

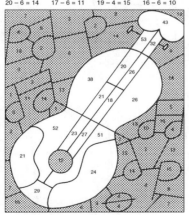

P 137

2 < or > 4	15 < or > 19	20 < or > 17	12 < or > 18
1 < or > 14	19 < or > 3	4 < or > 19	18 < or > 4
20 < or > 15	17 < or > 16	8 < or > 15	12 < or > 2
16 < or > 7	9 < or > 17	20 < or > 8	8 < or > 19

P 138

2 <u>4</u> 6 <u>8</u> <u>10</u> 12 <u>14</u> <u>16</u> <u>18</u> 20 <u>22</u> <u>24</u> <u>26</u> <u>28</u> <u>30</u> 32 <u>34</u> <u>36</u> <u>38</u> <u>40</u> <u>42</u> 44 <u>46</u> <u>48</u> <u>50</u> 52 <u>54</u> <u>56</u> <u>58</u> 60 <u>62</u> <u>64</u> <u>66</u> <u>68</u> <u>70</u> <u>72</u> <u>74</u> 76 <u>78</u> <u>80</u> <u>82</u> <u>84</u> <u>86</u> 88 <u>90</u> <u>92</u> <u>94</u> <u>96</u> <u>98</u> 100

P 139

5 <u>10</u> <u>15</u> <u>20</u> <u>25</u> <u>30</u> <u>35</u> <u>40</u> 45 <u>50</u> <u>55</u> <u>60</u> <u>65</u> <u>70</u> 75 <u>80</u> <u>85</u> <u>90</u> <u>95</u> <u>100</u>

P 140

10 <u>20</u> <u>30</u> <u>40</u> <u>50</u> 60 <u>70</u> <u>80</u> <u>90</u> <u>100</u> 110 <u>120</u> <u>130</u> 140 <u>150</u> <u>160</u> <u>170</u> <u>180</u> 190 <u>200</u>

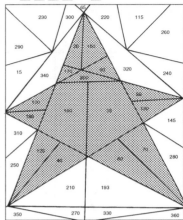

P 141

4 × 6 = 24	5 + 3 = 8	22 × 2 = 44	28 + 8 = 36
24 ÷ 4 = 6	7 × 6 = 42	9 − 7 = 2	8 × 8 = 64
22 − 2 = 20	25 × 5 = 30	4 + 6 = 10	11 − 2 = 9
5 × 1 = 5	7 + 4 = 11	18 − 18 = 0	15 + 5 = 3
33 − 7 = 26	45 − 14 = 31	35 × 1 = 35	80 ÷ 2 = 40

P 142

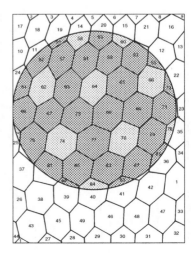

ANSWERS

P 143

18   25   104   1110

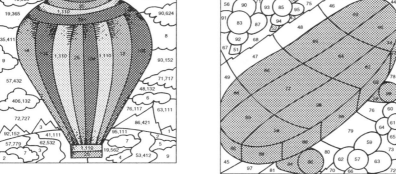

P 146

24	38	62	44	19	53
+62	+51	+37	+44	+50	+24
86	89	99	88	69	77

71	84	28	46	60	54
+13	+12	+30	+52	+22	+20
84	96	58	98	82	74

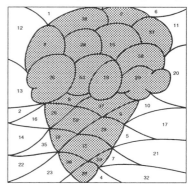

P 149

58	82	63	71	94	85
−29	−45	−37	−18	−36	−26
29	37	26	53	58	59

67	76	42	56	60	34
−58	−57	−14	−48	−22	−19
9	19	28	8	38	15

P 144

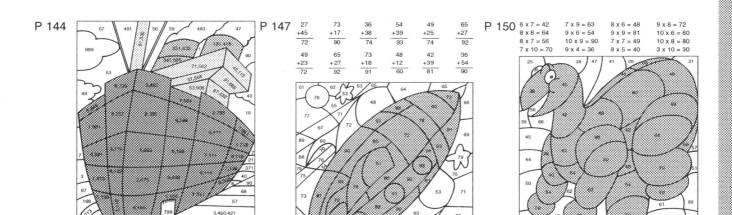

P 147

27	73	36	54	49	65
+45	+17	+38	+39	+25	+27
72	90	74	93	74	92

49	65	73	48	42	36
+23	+27	+18	+12	+39	+54
72	92	91	60	81	90

P 150

6 x 7 = 42	7 x 9 = 63	8 x 6 = 48	9 x 8 = 72
8 x 8 = 64	9 x 6 = 54	9 x 9 = 81	10 x 6 = 60
8 x 7 = 56	10 x 9 = 90	7 x 7 = 49	10 x 8 = 80
7 x 10 = 70	9 x 4 = 36	8 x 5 = 40	3 x 10 = 30

P 145

2 x 5 = 10	3 x 6 = 18	8 x 4 = 32	5 x 3 = 15
2 x 6 = 12	7 x 2 = 14	3 x 7 = 21	4 x 6 = 24
5 x 6 = 30	9 x 3 = 27	7 x 4 = 28	5 x 8 = 40
5 x 9 = 45	2 x 8 = 16	5 x 4 = 20	4 x 9 = 36

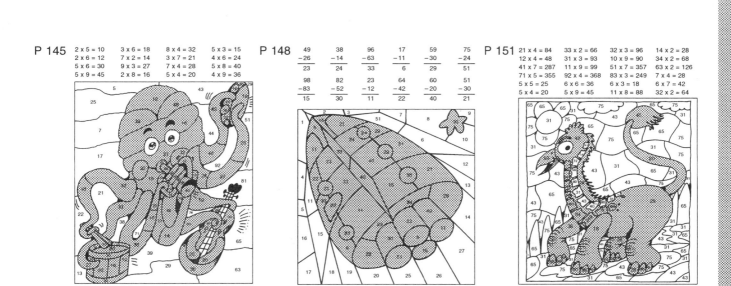

P 148

49	38	96	17	59	75
−26	−14	−63	−11	−30	−24
23	24	33	6	29	51

98	82	23	64	60	51
−83	−52	−12	−42	−20	−30
15	30	11	22	40	21

P 151

21 x 4 = 84	33 x 2 = 66	32 x 3 = 96	14 x 2 = 28
12 x 4 = 48	31 x 3 = 93	10 x 9 = 90	34 x 2 = 68
41 x 7 = 287	11 x 9 = 99	51 x 7 = 357	63 x 2 = 126
71 x 5 = 355	92 x 4 = 368	83 x 3 = 249	7 x 4 = 28
5 x 5 = 25	6 x 6 = 36	6 x 3 = 18	6 x 7 = 42
5 x 4 = 20	5 x 9 = 45	11 x 8 = 88	32 x 2 = 64

ANSWERS

P 152
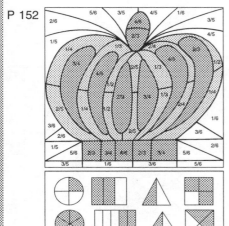

P 155

6.5	8.9	4.6	2.8	1.9	9.5
− 2.3	− 6.7	− 3.2	− 1.8	− 1.2	− 7.4
4.2	2.2	1.4	1.0	.7	2.1
7.4	5.7	34.9	54.6	78.1	64.7
− 5.1	− 4.4	− 12.6	− 31.4	− 42.0	− 51.3
2.3	1.3	22.3	23.2	36.1	13.4

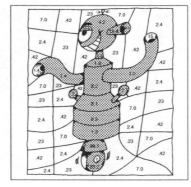

P 158

4 x 4 = 16	3 x 2 = 6	8 x 3 = 24	11 x 2 = 22
5 x 4 = 20	6 x 3 = 18	5 x 9 = 45	4 x 2 = 8
6 + 6 = 12	10 + 4 = 14	3 + 18 = 21	5 + 20 = 25
5 + 5 = 10	15 +15 = 30	24 + 8 = 32	18 + 18 = 36

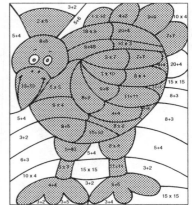

P 153

3/10	.3	6/10	.6
9/10	.9	2/10	.2
4/10	.4	1/10	.1
7/10	.7	5/10	.5
8/10	.8	10/10	1.0

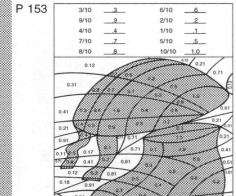

P 156

$7.50	$8.98	$4.66	$9.84	$2.19	$3.95
− 2.30	− 4.25	− 2.43	− 6.82	− 1.14	− 2.41
5.20	4.73	2.23	3.02	1.05	1.54
$5.74	$6.58	$7.38	$8.54	$6.93	$5.45
− 3.52	− 4.44	− 1.26	− 3.14	− 4.20	− 1.29
2.22	2.14	6.12	5.40	2.73	4.16

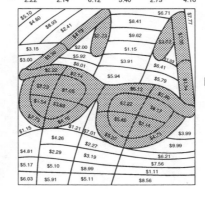

P 159
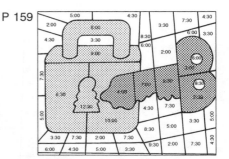

P 160
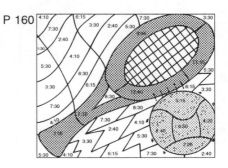

P 154

8.6	7.1	4.6	1.4	3.4	5.6
+1.2	+2.5	+5.3	+7.4	+4.2	+3.1
9.8	9.6	9.9	8.8	7.6	8.7
2.2	6.7	53.4	76.5	42.7	64.2
+4.6	+1.2	+32.5	+23.2	+47.1	+25.5
6.8	7.9	85.9	99.7	89.8	89.7

P 157

$3.80	$7.65	$8.37	$5.53	$4.74
+5.14	+2.23	+1.32	+2.46	+4.24
8.94	9.88	9.69	7.99	8.98
$2.58	$8.35	$6.32	$1.53	$4.55
+3.21	+1.62	+2.25	+3.25	+2.42
5.79	9.97	8.57	4.78	6.97
$2.77	$2.25			
+3.12	+2.54			
5.89	4.79			

P 161

16 ÷ 4 = 4	56 ÷ 7 = 8	6 ÷ 2 = 3	35 ÷ 7 = 5
63 ÷ 9 = 7	66 ÷ 11 = 6	12 ÷ 6 = 2	18 ÷ 2 = 9
88 ÷ 8 = 11	144 ÷ 12= 12	80 ÷ 8 = 10	12 ÷ 12 = 1

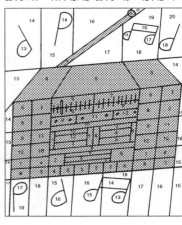

PRACTICE PAGE

PRACTICE PAGE

LANGUAGE ARTS

Nouns on Sale!
There are many different kinds of words. There are nouns, verbs, adjectives, and many others. A **noun** is a word that names a **person**, **place**, or **thing**. Look at the nouns in the word store. Write each one under the heading **Person**, **Place**, or **Thing**.

Person

_____

_____

_____

Place

_____

_____

_____

Thing

_____

_____

_____

Language Arts Skill: Identifying nouns

LANGUAGE ARTS

Common Nouns and Proper Nouns

Proper nouns are names. They begin with capital letters. Common nouns are just regular words. The word **dog** is a **common noun**. The word **Lassie** is a **proper noun**. Circle a proper noun in each sentence. Underline all the common nouns you can find.

My dog is called Tiny.

My cat is called Max.

I have a hamster named Frank.

Mom says we can't get any more pets.

I would really like a monkey, but Dad says, "No."

We take our animals to Dr. Miller, who is a veterinarian.

My cousin, Richard, is afraid of my hamster.

I go to Washington School.

My school is on State Street.

Mr. Kramer is my teacher.

My favorite pet in the classroom is a turtle named Spot.

We also have a rabbit, a gerbil, and Mike the fish.

Language Arts Skill: Identifying common and proper nouns

LANGUAGE ARTS

The Proper Nouns in Your Life
Complete this list with proper nouns. Remember! All proper nouns begin with capital letters.

Your name _____

The name of one or two people you live with _____

The name of a pet you have or would like to have _____

The name of the street where you live _____

The name of your town and state _____

Your teacher's name _____

The name of a friend you like very much _____

The name of a really good grown-up you know _____

How about this? *Look for proper nouns. Find names of people or places you know. Underline them in a school flyer, your town newspaper, a store ad, the church bulletin, or any other printed sheet of paper.*

Language Arts Skill: Using proper nouns

LANGUAGE ARTS

Pronouns that Mean You

Pronouns are short words that take the place of nouns. One pronoun you probably use a lot is the word **I**. Other pronouns that include you are **we**, **me**, **us**. Circle a pronoun in each sentence. Underline all the other nouns you can find.

Sometimes, I watch television alone.

Sometimes, I play games alone.

I play video games.

I like to make faces in the mirror.

I play games with my family, too.

We also read books together.

Sometimes, Dad reads to us.

Sometimes, Dad reads to just me all alone.

I like when Dad reads funny stories.

Sometimes, a friend reads with me.

Sometimes, we ask Mom to read a book.

Mom likes reading to us.

Language Arts Skill: Identifying pronouns

LANGUAGE ARTS

Pronouns that Mean <u>Other</u> People

Remember, **pronouns** take the place of nouns. Instead of using other people's names, you might use **she**, **he**, **her**, **him**, **they**, and **them**. Follow these directions to find all the nouns in the sentences below:

- Circle the pronouns that stand for other people.
- Draw a box around pronouns that stand for you.
- Underline all the common nouns.
- Put a star above all the proper nouns.

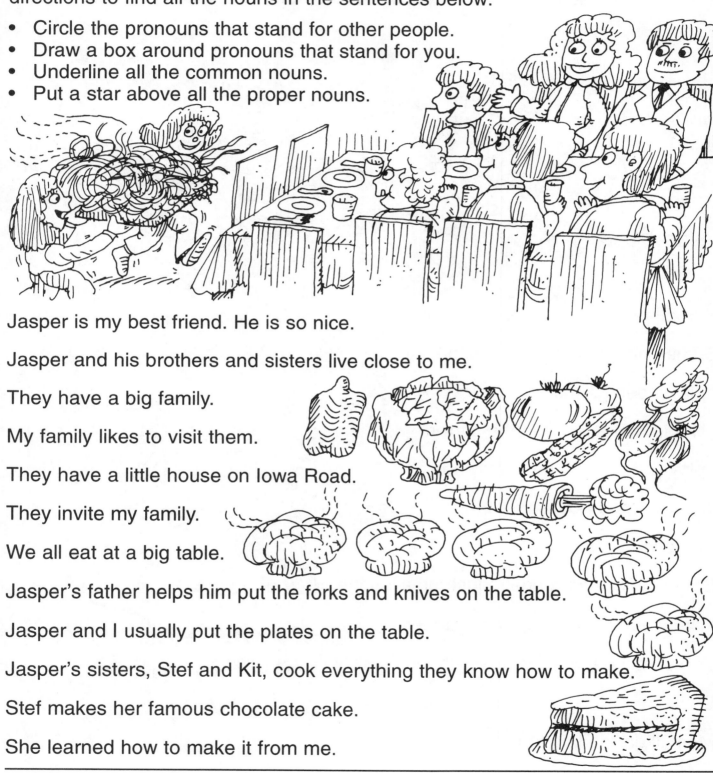

Jasper is my best friend. He is so nice.

Jasper and his brothers and sisters live close to me.

They have a big family.

My family likes to visit them.

They have a little house on Iowa Road.

They invite my family.

We all eat at a big table.

Jasper's father helps him put the forks and knives on the table.

Jasper and I usually put the plates on the table.

Jasper's sisters, Stef and Kit, cook everything they know how to make.

Stef makes her famous chocolate cake.

She learned how to make it from me.

Language Arts Skill: Identifying pronouns, nouns, and proper nouns

LANGUAGE ARTS

It—A Great Way to Save Time!
Another important pronoun is **it**. This super-short word comes in handy when you are in a hurry! Instead of saying "house," "animal," or whatever, you can say **it**. (There are some animals you wouldn't call **it**. Usually, you call a pet **he** or **she**.)

Write a pronoun you might use instead of the noun.

Your name _____

Mr. Gremlin _____

Mrs. North _____

A policeman _____

A wild wolf _____

Lisa, Josh, Tony _____

A mystery note _____

A boarded-up house _____

A bowl of poisonous vapor _____

Your next-door neighbor's girl poodle, Puffette _____

Language Arts Skill: Recognizing pronouns

171

LANGUAGE ARTS

What's Mine is Mine...
Words such as **my**, **mine**, **your**, **yours**, **his**, and **hers** are also pronouns. They are a quick way of saying that something belongs to somebody. But you don't have to say the person's name.

Use the pronouns above to fill in the blanks in this story.

      Somebody found a cap at the boarded-up haunted house! The cap doesn't belong to Mrs. North. It is not _____. The cap doesn't belong to Mr. Gremlin. It is not_____. A man outside the boarded-up house said the cap was not_____. That cap fits me because it is _____! The cap that belongs to you fits_____head. But how did_____cap get to the boarded-up house? I didn't leave it there. I think the house is haunted by the ghost of Captain Roberto. It is_____ house. Captain Roberto's head is much bigger than _____. I don't know why he wanted my small hat. ____hat fits him perfectly.

How about this? Tell someone a story explaining how the cap got to the haunted house. Ask them to clap their hands every time you use a pronoun.

Language Arts Skill: Identifying possessive pronouns and using them to write

LANGUAGE ARTS

Possessions!

To say that something belongs to someone, add an –'s or an –s' to their name. How do you know which one to use? If one person owns the thing, add –'s. If a whole group of people own the thing, add –s'.

The boy's bike   The boys' boat

Read the sentences. Look at the possessive nouns below them. Choose the correct possessive noun and write it in the blank.

_____ dog likes to run and jump.
Ellens'   Ellen's

_____ cat likes to hiss and spit.
Kathys'   Kathy's

This is Frank. This is _____ gross foot.
Franks'   Frank's

Here are both _____ backpacks.
girls'   girl's

This is Lisa. This is _____ cap.
Lisas'   Lisa's

These are the puppies. This is the _____ mother.
puppie's   puppies'

Language Arts Skill: Using singular and plural possessive nouns

LANGUAGE ARTS

Double or Nothing

Lessie has one of everything—one pencil, one lunch, one penny. Tessie has one of everything, too—one pencil, one lunch, one penny. When they get together, everything goes plural! Look at the list of things Lessie and Tessie have. Then write the plurals by adding **–s**, **–es**, or **–ies**. Be careful! Some words may need special attention!

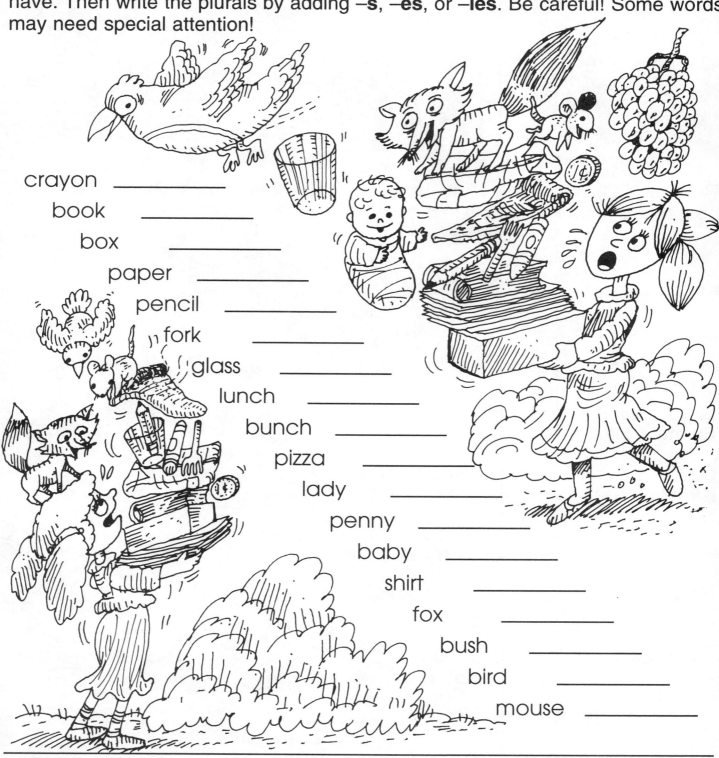

crayon _____

book _____

box _____

paper _____

pencil _____

fork _____

glass _____

lunch _____

bunch _____

pizza _____

lady _____

penny _____

baby _____

shirt _____

fox _____

bush _____

bird _____

mouse _____

Language Arts Skill: Creating plural nouns

LANGUAGE ARTS

What to Do, What to Do

Nouns name a person, place, or thing. **Verbs** often tell what a noun is doing. A verb can show action. Think of all the action you do in one day.

jump

run

eat

read

Underline the verb in each sentence.

Jake walks.

Sam runs everywhere he goes.

Hettie dances to the music on the radio.

Calvin spins around and around the room.

Anthony claps his hands.

Ashley draws a picture.

Nicole snaps her fingers.

The dog wags its tail.

The cat purrs.

The wind blows around the house.

The snow falls in a thick white blanket.

The grandfather clock strikes 9:00.

sing

look

Language Arts Skill: Identifying verbs

LANGUAGE ARTS

Action!

You are the director of a movie. You are also the story-writer. Write a **verb** that shows interesting action for each character.

Mr. Turpentine_____ to the door and starts yelling.

Ms. Stepenlocket_____ and says, "Why is this happening?"

Ms. Galvanize _____ a large object from the basement.

Count Gorko_____ and refuses to speak.

The baby_____ as he talks into the toy telephone.

Make up a story using some of the characters from above and some of your own characters. After reading your story, underline a verb in each sentence.

_____

_____

_____

_____

_____

_____

_____

_____

Language Arts Skill: Using verbs

LANGUAGE ARTS

Verbs and Music

Sometimes, verbs end in –s. Sometimes they don't.

> **Add –s:** He sings. She sings. It sings. Ted sings.
> **Don't add –s:** I sing. You sing. We sing. They sing.

Write a word from the end of the line in the blank.

Max _____ the guitar. (**play, plays**)

I _____ with the band. (**sing, sings**)

Sophie and Jet _____ the drums. (**pound, pounds**)

They _____ two hours a day. (**practice, practices**)

Meadowlark _____ music. (**read, reads**)

My friends _____ their fingers when the band starts playing. (**tap, taps**)

You can _____ beautiful sounds coming from Jamie's harmonica.

   (**hear, hears**)

He _____ down close to the floor when he plays. (**bend, bends**)

People _____ when he is finished playing. (**clap, claps**)

Ringo _____ too because Jamie is so good. (**clap, claps**)

We all _____ to our favorite groups on CDs. (**listen, listens**)

Language Arts Skill: Using verbs in the present tense

177

LANGUAGE ARTS

Been There, Done That

When a word describes what is happening right now, we say it is in the **present tense**. When it describes something that happened before, we say it is in the **past tense**. You can add an **–ed** to a verb to tell about something that happened before.

Underline a verb in each sentence.

I walk to school.
I walked yesterday.

My dog barks as I leave for school.
My dog barked really loudly this morning.

My mom and dad wave to me when I leave.
Yesterday, I waved back at them.

When we were in kindergarten, we played a lot in school.
Now we play only at special times.

I add lots of numbers and check the answer on my calculator.
Only last week, I added a column of ten numbers.

After school, I painted a mural showing my neighborhood.
I paint the sun to finish my picture.

Write the verbs you underlined in the correct column below.

Present tense verbs   **Past tense verbs**

_____   _____

_____   _____

_____   _____

_____   _____

_____   _____

_____   _____

Language Arts Skill: Identifying present and past tense verbs

178

LANGUAGE ARTS

What Is Irregular?

Irregular means weird. Irregular verbs are weird verbs. To change them from the present tense to the past tense, it's not enough to add **–ed**. Look at the list of irregular verbs. Use the words in the list to fill in the blanks below.

Present	Past
run	ran
come	came
give	gave
make	made
take	took
speak	spoke
sing	sang
fly	flew
swim	swam
wear	wore
see	saw
say	said

I _____ home from school every day.

Yesterday, I _____ faster than I ever did.

I _____ in the old pool every day last summer.

Now, I _____ in a new pool near my house.

Last week, I _____ to the librarian about tarantulas.

Today, I _____ to her about scorpions.

Now you _____ me jump over the fence.

I _____ you do it many times.

Yesterday, we _____ our music books out into the school yard.

Today, we _____ our math books.

I _____ Mom's hat yesterday.

I _____ my own hat now.

Language Arts Skill: Using irregular verbs

LANGUAGE ARTS

Verbs that Just Sit Around

You can usually tell a verb because it names something you can do—like run, jump, sleep, and eat. But some verbs don't do anything at all! Some of these verbs are **is**, **are**, **am**, **was**, and **were**.

Write one of these verbs in each sentence.

I _____ good at many things.

He _____ good at many things.

She _____ good at many things.

They _____ good at many things.

I _____ thinking very hard.

They _____ going to Little League together.

I _____ going with them.

But they _____ leaving too early.

She _____ climbing the tree.

They _____ going to try to climb the tree.

I _____ trying to climb it yesterday.

Many kids _____ trying to climb the tree.

Language Arts Skill: Using the irregular verb to be

LANGUAGE ARTS

Looking Ahead

Verbs can tell about the **present** and the **past**. But did you know that they can tell about the **future**, too? If you see the word **will**, the verb that comes next is talking about what's going to happen. Look at the verbs in bold in the story below. Circle the verbs that tell about the future. Put an X over verbs that tell about the past.

I **visit** my Aunt Fatima all the time. Yesterday, Aunt Fatima **visited** a fortune-teller! Tomorrow, I **will visit** the fortune-teller, too.

Aunt Fatima **tells** me whatever she thinks. Yesterday, Aunt Fatima **told** me that the fortune-teller was magic! "She **will tell** you amazing things," Aunt Fatima said.

Dad and I **drove** to the fortune-teller's house. My dad **drives** pretty fast. Someday, I **will drive** a little slower.

I **was** a little nervous this morning. Dad says he **is** a little nervous now. But the fortune-teller **will be** very kind, Aunt Fatima promised.

I **saw** someone inside the fortune-teller's window! And I **see** Aunt Fatima's car parked outside! Could Aunt Fatima be the fortune-teller I **will see** today?

How About This? You don't have to be a fortune-teller to think about the future. What do you think you will be like when you get older? Write about it, using **will** as often as you like.

Language Arts Skill: Identifying verbs in the future, past, and present tense

LANGUAGE ARTS

A Verb Hunt
Underline all the **verbs** you can find in the sentences.

Callie eats cereal with chocolate on it. Etsuko enjoys crab apples. Jake and Jim were at the store. They bought cereal, chocolate, and crab apples for their friends.

Shereena is a character in a tall tale. She was as tall as a big oak tree. She made her clothes out of tree trunks. She jumped so high people thought she was flying.

When my cousin comes to town, we all hide. His mother says he is a good boy. I think he is good only when he sleeps. My cousin cuts up strips of newspaper just for fun. Then he eats them! My cousin is a little bit strange.

Language Arts Skill: Identifying verbs

LANGUAGE ARTS

Fascinating Action

Really good writers don't just use the same old verbs over and over. That would be boring. There are so many interesting verbs to pick from! Look at the list of interesting words that mean **said**. Use them to make the story below more exciting.

cried   wept   shouted   hollered   screamed
hissed   whispered   groaned   explained

"What are you talking about?" _____ Merlin with tears
   running down his face.

"Just cool down now," _____ Gunga.

"Yes," _____ Pluto, "you are getting me annoyed."

"You all have very bad manners," _____ Flatney.

Write two interesting verbs that mean the same thing as the word at the top of each list.

walked   **ate**   **spoke**   **made**

_____   _____   _____   _____

_____   _____   _____   _____

Language Arts Skill: Using synonyms creatively

183

LANGUAGE ARTS

Get Creative!
Look at the words in the treasure chest. What a zany bunch of words! Find words in the treasure chest that could be used instead of the less interesting words at the top of each list. If you don't know what a word means, why not look it up in the dictionary?

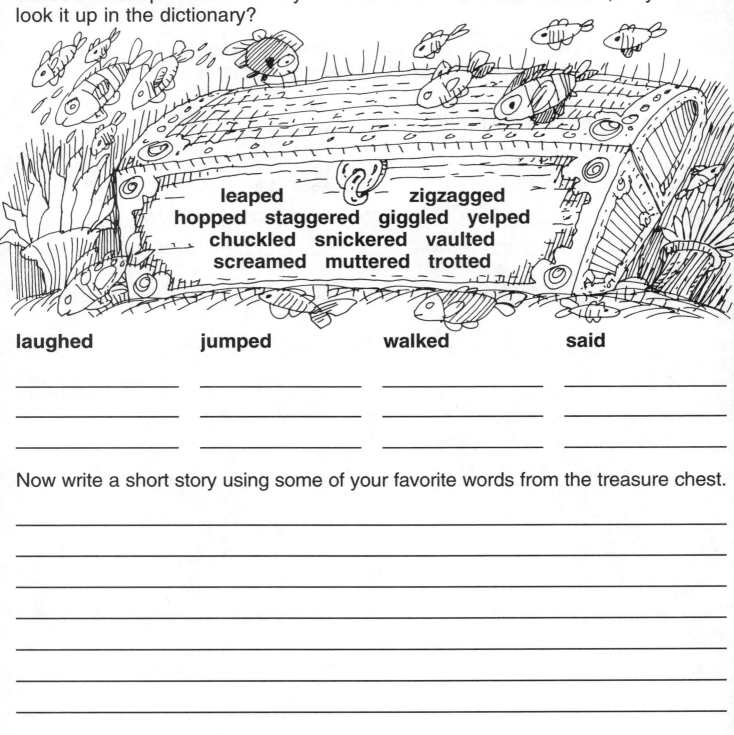

leaped   zigzagged
hopped   staggered   giggled   yelped
chuckled   snickered   vaulted
screamed   muttered   trotted

laughed   **jumped**   **walked**   **said**

_____ _____ _____ _____

_____ _____ _____ _____

_____ _____ _____ _____

Now write a short story using some of your favorite words from the treasure chest.

_____

_____

_____

_____

_____

_____

_____

_____

_____

Language Arts Skill: Using colorful language creatively

LANGUAGE ARTS

Adjectives: The Spice of Life!

Jimmy-Bob was writing sentences. **The dog chased the cat**, he wrote. But that's so boring, he thought. Jimmy-Bob needed some good **adjectives**. Adjectives are words that describe nouns. Choosing the right adjectives can make what you say and write more interesting.

The dog chased the cat.

The **tiny**, **yapping** dog chased the **gigantic**, **monstrous** cat.

Circle a noun and underline one or more adjectives that describe the noun.

Amy wore a red sweater.

Christopher has on big, old shoes.

Jessica wears tiny, blue earrings.

Anthony wears a huge jacket.

David clomps around in heavy, brown boots.

That is Amanda's beautiful, green umbrella.

I saw Daniel's shiny, new sunglasses.

Maisie wears unusual clothing.

Christopher likes his squeaky running shoes.

Everyone likes to copy clever, creative Maisie.

How about this? *Draw a cool girl or cool boy poster of yourself. Make a border of words to describe the way you look. Describe your eyes, your hair, your clothes, and everything! For example,* **sleepy eyes**, **curly hair**, **wrinkled shirt***!*

Language Arts Skill: Identifying adjectives

LANGUAGE ARTS

Verbs and Adverbs

Vanessa is watching the exciting action at the circus. She is writing it all down, but it doesn't sound exciting on paper. Vanessa needs some **adverbs**. Adverbs go with verbs, and they help describe how an action was done. Many adverbs end in **–ly**.

The clown fell and smiled.

The clown fell **awkwardly** and laughed **crazily**.

Circle a verb and underline the adverb. Draw a box around two adverbs that don't end with **–ly**.

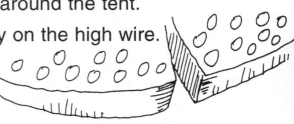

The clown ate greedily.

Another clown behaved grossly.

The crowd yelled harshly.

The ballerina danced gracefully.

The master of ceremonies spoke often.

The people smiled happily.

The elephants walked slowly around the tent.

The acrobats worked carefully on the high wire.

The young boy juggled well.

The lion tamer ran quickly.

Language Arts Skill: Identifying adverbs

LANGUAGE ARTS

Cyclops Sentences

Read each sentence in this tale of bravery! One word is missing. Look at the words after the sentence. Which one fits? Write it in the blank.

Everyone _____ that a Cyclops is a round, ugly creature with
    one eye in the middle of his head. (**know, knows**)

It was getting dark when I first saw this _____ monster. (**scary, scarily**)

He came _____ toward me. (**slow, slowly**)

He gurgled _____. (**horrible, horribly**)

He had one huge ____ eye in the middle of his head. (**foot, red**)

I _____ slowly around the Cyclops. (**circle, circled**)

I waved my long, skinny, _____fingers in the air. (**claw-like, claws**)

I _____ at the Cyclops. (**jump, jumped**)

The Cyclops leaped back _____. (**clumsy, clumsily**)

Then he walked away, shaking ____ head. (**their, his**)

When I saw his _____ eyes, I was sorry. (**sad, sadly**)

But then the Cyclops shook his head at _____. (**my, me**)

"I'll be back!" he roared _____. (**loud, loudly**)

I hate to admit it, but I was about to run away as _____ as I
    could! (**quick, quickly**)

But then the Cyclops _____. (**disappearing, disappeared**)

Language Arts Skill: Using nouns, verbs, adjectives, and adverbs

LANGUAGE ARTS

Your Ears Can't Tell the Difference

Sir Homonym knows all about **homonyms**. They are words that sound alike, but are spelled differently. They also mean different things. Read the story below. Underline two words that are homonyms in each sentence.

On special festivals, lots of knights meet to eat meat pies.

Sir Homonym was known as the one who won pie-eating contests.

At one festival, Sir Homonym ate eight whole pies.

Once, he saved my aunt from an attack of a man-eating ant.

She was so grateful that she decided to sew him a new shopping bag full of pies.

She would not pay one cent to have the bag sent through the mail.

My aunt walked for four miles and left the bag on Sir Homonym's doorstep.

The knight came home very late that night.

A mist covered the land, so he missed the pie bag lying on the doorstep.

When the horse tripped over the pie bag, the knight yelled in a hoarse voice.

You never heard a grown man groan like Sir Homonym did when he fell

off the horse.

But when his nose smelled the pies, he cried, "Pies in a bag! Somebody

knows what I like!"

"Oh, my!" he whispered after he took his first bite. "I must owe someone a big

thank-you note for these."

Right away he sat down to write my aunt a very nice card.

Language Arts Skill: Identifying homonyms

LANGUAGE ARTS

Dull Is Definitely Not Nice

Nice, nice, nice—what a boring word! Why not say **fabulous** or **beautiful** or **terrific**? You can make your writing more interesting by using **synonyms**. Synonyms are different words that mean the same thing. If you know a synonym for a word, you don't have to keep using the same word over and over again.

Draw lines to connect the words that are synonyms.

look	grab
like	twist
make	enjoy
turn	shiver
shake	locate
find	watch
take	build

Fill in each blank with a synonym from the word box.

> **funny   noise   teensy   sick
> scary   piece   enormous**

little _____   sound _____

part _____   large _____

ill _____   silly _____

creepy _____

Write two sentences. Use two synonyms in the sentences.

_____

_____

_____

Language Arts Skill: Identifying synonyms

189

LANGUAGE ARTS

Opposites

Anti and Khan never agree. If Anti says **round**, Khan says **flat**. If Khan says **top**, Anti says **bottom**. These words are all **antonyms**. That means they have opposite meanings. Write an antonym from the box for each word on the list.

finish	enemy	off
cold	dazzling	under
disgusting	late	

on   _____

start   _____

hot   _____

over   _____

early   _____

friend   _____

lovely   _____

boring   _____

Think of your own opposites! Look at the pairs of sentences below. Use antonyms to fill in the blanks.

Anti says a science lesson about how grass grows is _____.

But Khan thinks the lesson could be really _____.

Khan gave me a _____ poster of flowers for my birthday.

Anti gave me a _____ rubber chicken!

Anti likes to sing songs that sound _____.

Khan prefers to play his guitar to songs that are _____.

Now you write two sentences using a pair of antonyms.

_____

_____

_____

Language Arts Skill: Using antonyms

LANGUAGE ARTS

Anti and Khan Still Disagree

Anti and Khan can't even agree about how to do the simplest things. They are trying to describe some actions. Read the adverbs Anti chooses to describe the action. Then look at the antonyms in the word box. Which one would Khan choose to describe the same action?

	sloppily gently well wisely carelessly quickly clumsily quietly	

Anti says:

Anti says:		Khan says:
roughly	**pet the kitten**	_____
slowly	**wake up and stretch**	_____
gracefully	**turn cartwheels**	_____
carefully	**carry the pitcher**	_____
neatly	**wipe your mouth**	_____
loudly	**whistle a tune**	_____
foolishly	**behave in class**	_____
poorly	**weed the garden**	_____

Write a verb and an adverb to describe the same person on a good day and a bad day.

Good Day

dressed neatly

_____

_____

_____

Bad Day

dressed sloppily

_____

_____

_____

Language Arts Skill: Identifying adverb antonyms

191

LANGUAGE ARTS

Using the Right Word
Pavel doesn't like to make mistakes. But these sentences have him confused!
Help him by circling the correct word for each sentence.

Josh sang **bad / badly** because he had a cold.

Mandy walks **slow / slowly** down the hall.

That **boy's / boys'** dog is very cute.

All the **boy's / boys'** jackets were left on the playground.

She lost just one **tooth / teeth** this year.

Many **woman / women** came to see the third grade show.

Kevin **wash / washed** every dish in the sink.

Jack and Jill **gives / gave** their friend some stickers.

Jessie **brush / brushes** her hair every morning.

Mac **wish / wishes** he could get a new mitt for his birthday.

Sarah counted all the **pennys / pennies** in her bank.

If you have ever **seen / saw** a giraffe, you know they are big.

Freddy and Ginger **seen / saw** their neighbors at the pool.

Sam **give / gave** Michelle two books to the school book sale.

Justin spoke **quick / quickly** because he was excited.

Language Arts Skill: Using nouns, verbs, and adverbs

LANGUAGE ARTS

No Time to Waste

Sophie is always in a hurry. She is always looking for shortcuts. She knows that sometimes you can save time by writing two words as one word. That's called using a contraction. These are her favorites.

aren't didn't can't haven't wouldn't doesn't

Write a contraction from the list for each word phrase.

are not _____   can not _____

did not _____   have not _____

would not _____   does not _____

Draw a line connecting each word phrase with it's contraction.

it is   you're

she is   he's

he is   it's

who is   we're

they are   she's

you are   who's

we are   they're

How about this? *The word phrase* **will not** *has an unusual contraction. It is spelled* **won't**. *Can you write a story about a stubborn mule using* **won't** *three times?*

Language Arts Skill: Using contractions

LANGUAGE ARTS

Shortcuts Galore

Sameena's pencil is a tiny stub! But she still has a lot to write. To make her pencil last longer, she wants to use contractions wherever she can. Help her by writing a contraction in each sentence.

Some Things About Some Kids

Ferdinand _____ whistle and spit at the same time.

Wee Willie Winkie _____ go to bed on time.

The brothers Gerk and Geek say _____ not really brothers.

They say they _____ even related.

Doorchester is always saying, "Knock, knock, _____ there?"

My friend Halo and I always tell people that _____ best friends.

The evil twins said they _____ even in the room when the
    fish tank fell.

My cat _____ eat mice, because she's too refined and elegant.

People often would say I need a bath, but I _____ agree.

Drusilla is the one _____ standing on her head.

When someone says, "Why did you do that?" I always say,

    "I _____ a clue."

How about this? *Sometimes people use contractions that are not right. One incorrect contraction you might hear is* ***ain't***. *What do people mean when they say* ***ain't***? *What contraction is the right one to use instead?*

Language Arts Skill: Using contractions

LANGUAGE ARTS

Anna and an Article

Anna is writing an article for the school newspaper. She knows that sometimes you use **a** and sometimes you use **an** in front of a noun. But she's not sure what the difference is. The answer is easy! All you have to do is say the noun out loud.

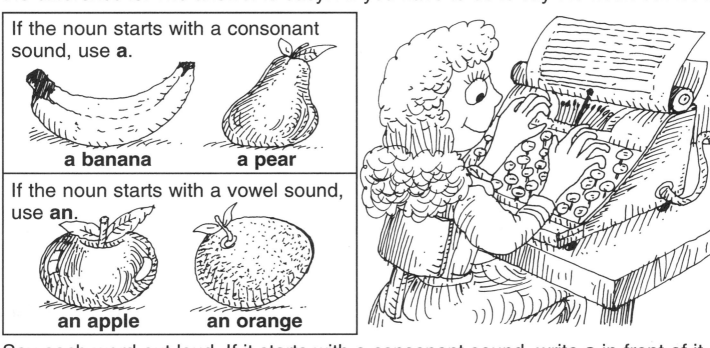

If the noun starts with a consonant sound, use **a**.

a banana   **a pear**

If the noun starts with a vowel sound, use **an**.

an apple   **an orange**

Say each word out loud. If it starts with a consonant sound, write **a** in front of it. If it starts with a vowel sound, write **an** in front of it.

_____ ape   _____ gorilla

_____ puppy   _____ orangutan

_____ elephant   _____ trunk

_____ soda   _____ ice cube

_____ egg   _____ creature

_____ game board   _____ abacus

_____ elf   _____ fairy

_____ umbrella   _____ raincoat

_____ sneaker   _____ illusion

How about this? *A story in a newspaper or a magazine is called an* **article**. *But there is another meaning for* **article**. *The words* **a**, **an**, *and* **the** *are also called* **articles**! *Read an article in a newspaper or magazine. Whenever you see* **a**, **an**, *or* **the**, *circle the word. How many are there in all?*

Language Arts Skill: Using the articles a and an

LANGUAGE ARTS

An Amazing Party for a Special Troll
It's time for the annual troll party! You know to say **a troll**, not **an troll**, of course.
But what if there's an **adjective** in front of troll? How do you make up your mind
whether to use **a** or **an**? Just listen to the beginning sound of the adjective!

If the adjective starts with a consonant sound, use **a**.

a lovely troll

If the adjective starts with a vowel sound, use **an**.

an ugly troll

Choose an adjective for each guest on the list below. Then decide to use **a** or **an**.

icky
evil
ghastly
scary
enormous
screeching
decaying
toothless
alarming
one-eyed
foul-smelling

The Annual Troll Party Guest List

a or an	adjective	guest
_____	_____	witch
_____	_____	Cyclops
_____	_____	owl
_____	_____	mummy
_____	_____	ghost
_____	_____	vampire
_____	_____	wizard
_____	_____	vulture
_____	_____	skeleton

How about this? *Draw a mural of scary and ridiculous party guests and print the
name of each near its picture. Add an article and a really good adjective. Hang up
the mural where you sleep. Pleasant dreams!*

Language Arts Skill: Using articles with adjectives and nouns

LANGUAGE ARTS

Titles Need Capital Letters

You know that proper nouns always have capital letters—for example, names like Judy Doormouse and Anthony McDooglehammer, and places like New York City and the Pacific Ocean. But did you know that the titles that go in front of a name also have capital letters? Here are some.

> Ms. Mr. Mrs. Miss Dr. Judge Officer
> Professor Queen King Emperor

Look at this list. What letters should have capitals? Use a crayon or a colored pencil to turn all the wrong lowercase letters into capitals. Don't forget the place names!

Mr. means Mister.
Mrs. means Missus.
Dr. means Doctor.
You can say Ms.
as Miz.

- mr. hank snodgrass
- king swaddlebottom
- dr. sally pilladay
- judge a. bythebook
- professor thomas takeahike
- officer putcherhandsup
- miss lynn forkitover
- queen ann of bonjour, france
- good eats restaurant and gas
- slamdunk city, texas
- boondoggle elementary school
- emperor hinglesnaffer whatchamacallit
- lotsalaughs comedy club in kneeslapper, iowa

How about this? Words like **king** have capitals only if they are attached to a specific person's name. For example, **King Bob is in town**. **The king would like a snack**. Try writing sentence pairs like that for **princess** and **Dr**. Don't forget to spell out **doctor** when it is lower case! Ask a grown-up to look at your sentences.

Language Arts Skill: Using capital letters for titles

LANGUAGE ARTS

Capitalization

Globetrotter Greg of Boston, Massachussets, is leaving on Monday for a big trip to visit his friends. He is writing down his travel plans for his mom and dad. But he forgot that names, days of the week, months, cities, states, and countries all have capital letters. Can you circle all the letters that he forgot to make capital?

People I will visit:

- monday, october 12: sam hammenegg in houston, texas
- saturday, december 8: dr. juan stetoskopes in acapulco, mexico
- tuesday, february 23: miss zha zha vavavoom in paris, france
- wednesday, may 5: sir dingo stark in manchester, england
- sunday, july 18: ms. hoagie jean in philadelphia, pennsylvania
- friday, august 30: mr. mehta sumit in new delhi, india
- thursday, september 27: tete makesela in morondava, madagascar

How about this? *Look up all of these place names on a map or a globe. Which is the closest to Greg's home in Boston, Massachussets? Which is the farthest away? If you see any other interesting place names, write them down in a list. Then you can look for books about them, or even make a visit!*

Language Arts Skill: Using capital letters

LANGUAGE ARTS

Postcards, Postcards, and More Postcards

Globetrotter Greg knows how to use commas when he writes postcards to his mom and dad. A comma comes between the number for the date and the number for the year, as in **March 8, 2000**. A comma also comes between the name of a city and the name of a state or country, as in **Chicago, Illinois**, and **Rome, Italy**.

Add commas where they belong on these postcards.

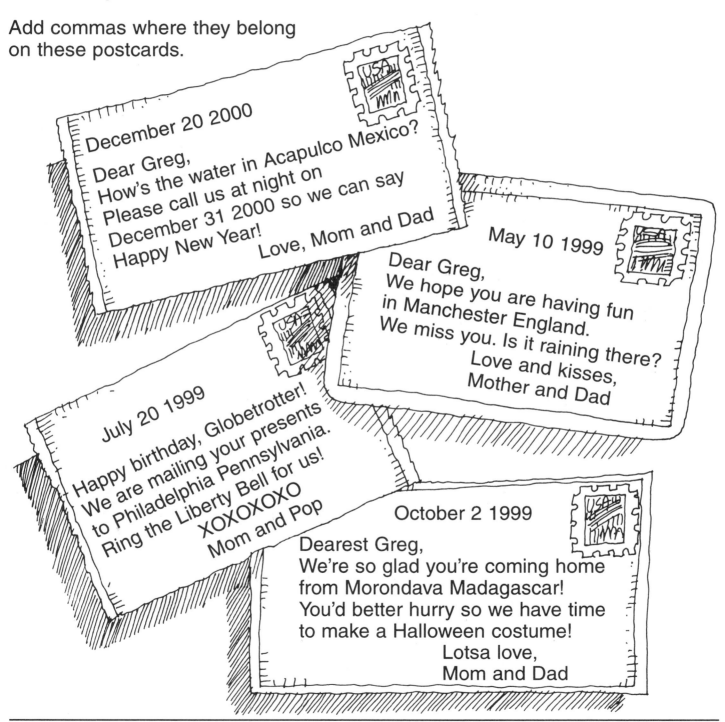

December 20 2000

Dear Greg,
How's the water in Acapulco Mexico?
Please call us at night on
December 31 2000 so we can say
Happy New Year!
Love, Mom and Dad

May 10 1999

Dear Greg,
We hope you are having fun
in Manchester England.
We miss you. Is it raining there?
Love and kisses,
Mother and Dad

July 20 1999

Happy birthday, Globetrotter!
We are mailing your presents
to Philadelphia Pennsylvania.
Ring the Liberty Bell for us!
XOXOXOXO
Mom and Pop

October 2 1999

Dearest Greg,
We're so glad you're coming home
from Morondava Madagascar!
You'd better hurry so we have time
to make a Halloween costume!
Lotsa love,
Mom and Dad

Language Arts Skill: Using commas

LANGUAGE ARTS

Words in a Row

Raquel is going to visit her grandparents. She is packing lots of things. Look at the list of what she is packing. When Raquel lists many things in a row, she knows to put a comma between each thing, with the word **and** before the last thing. When she reads the list, she knows to pause every time she comes to a comma.

shirts, socks, scuba diving equipment, jeans, hairbrush, bathing suit, flip flops, soccer ball, and toothbrush

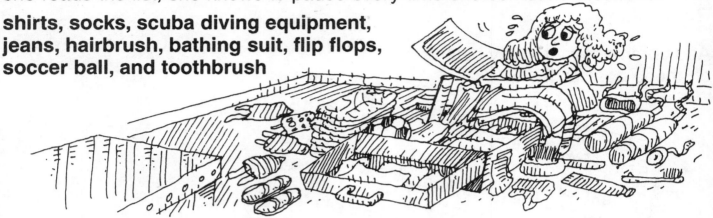

Read each sentence. Put commas between the words in the list. Don't forget the comma before **and**!

> In my backpack I have paper pencils money and cards.
> I like to travel in cars trains buses and planes.
> I sent cards to Sara Patty Kevin and Jamal.

You can plan a trip, too! Write your own lists to finish these sentences about a great vacation.

In my suitcase I will pack _____

_____

_____.

In my backpack I will pack _____

_____

_____.

I plan on going to _____

_____

_____

Language Arts Skill: Using capitalization and commas in writing

LANGUAGE ARTS

Who's There? What's That?

The **subject** is **who** or **what** is doing something in a sentence. Read the sentences below. Then answer the question about the subject of the sentence.

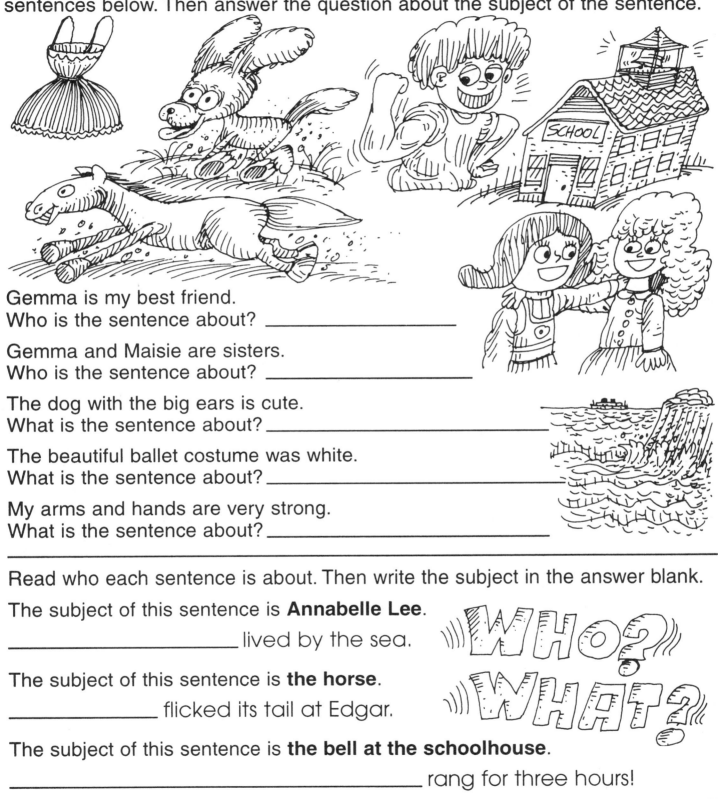

Gemma is my best friend.
Who is the sentence about? _____

Gemma and Maisie are sisters.
Who is the sentence about? _____

The dog with the big ears is cute.
What is the sentence about? _____

The beautiful ballet costume was white.
What is the sentence about? _____

My arms and hands are very strong.
What is the sentence about? _____

Read who each sentence is about. Then write the subject in the answer blank.

The subject of this sentence is **Annabelle Lee**.

_____ lived by the sea.

The subject of this sentence is **the horse**.

_____ flicked its tail at Edgar.

The subject of this sentence is **the bell at the schoolhouse**.

_____ rang for three hours!

Language Arts Skill: Identifying all the words that make up the subject

LANGUAGE ARTS

What's the Subject?

The **subject** is **who** or **what** is doing something in the sentence. Look at the sentences below. Circle the people or things that are doing the action.

Grandma is reading a story to me.

She and I are curled up in the big chair.

The book fell onto the floor!

My pet monkey picked it up and gave it back.

The story was very exciting.

It started, "Once upon a time…"

The Three Little Pigs needed some exercise.

Snortly the Pig ran out into the woods.

Gortly the Pig and Portly the Pig ran after him.

They all ran very slowly.

The Big Bad Wolf smiled and licked his lips and put on running shoes.

He ran very quickly through the forest.

Suddenly his feet started to hurt!

The running shoes squished the Big Bad Wolf's toes.

He sat down on a log to take off his shoes.

Then he went home to soak his feet in the bathtub.

The Three Little Pigs got away—this time!

Language Arts Skill: Identifying the subject of a sentence

202

LANGUAGE ARTS

Pigs and Wolves: Living in Harmony?
You can read more about the Pig family and its troubles. But these sentences have no subjects! Read each paragraph. Then look at the word box. Use the subjects in the word box to finish the sentences.

_____ are the three Pig brothers.
_____ is their neighbor. _____ are not the best of friends. _____ between their houses is 15 feet tall.

> **They**
> **The fence**
> **Snortly, Gortly, and Portly**
> **The Big Bad Wolf**

One day, _____ throw a party. _____ is ready. _____ arrive on time. But when Portly turns on the music, nothing happens! _____ is broken!

> **All of the food**
> **Portly's stereo**
> **The guests**
> **the Pig brothers**

Suddenly, _____ hears some beautiful music. _____ comes floating over the 15-foot fence. It must be coming from the Big Bad Wolf's house, he thinks! Together, _____ _____ tiptoe outside and peek around the fence. _____ is sitting right there in the yard! And the wolf is playing it.

> **A piano**
> **Gortly**
> **Gortly, Snortly, and Portly**
> **A lovely tune**

What do you think happens next? Write an ending for the story on a fresh piece of paper. Make sure all of your sentences have subjects!

Language Arts Skill: Identifying singular and plural subjects

LANGUAGE ARTS

Dance of the Prancing Predicates

Hammernoggin and Lumbertoes dance every day. **Dance every day** is what they are doing. That means that **dance every day** is the **predicate**. A predicate tells what the subject is doing. It always has a verb in it.

Hammernoggin and Lumbertoes made up a dance. You can read about it below. But there are no predicates! Look at the box of predicates. Fill one into each blank. Make sure each answer fits! Then try out the dance with a friend.

> • **hoot like wild hungry monsters** • **hops in a circle around his friend**
> • **squirms like a snake around his friend** • **flap their arms three times**
> • **kick their legs up as high as they can six times**

First, Hammernoggin and Lumbertoes _____
_____. Then Hammernoggin _____
_____. Then Lumbertoes _____
_____. Standing back to back, they both _____
_____.

Finally, they spin in a big circle and _____
_____.

Language Arts Skill: Adding predicates to make complete sentences

A Complete Monster

A sentence is a complete thought. It tells what is happening and who or what is doing it. Read each line below. Does it sound like a complete thought to you? If you can answer both the questions below it, it is a full sentence. Put a star next to each full sentence.

1. Who or what is doing something?   2. What is he/she/it doing?

The monster is eating yellow worms.

1. _____   2. _____

Orange, yellow, and green worms.

1. _____   2. _____

The worms try to wiggle away.

1. _____   2. _____

Roared and grabbed the worms.

1. _____   2. _____

The monster swallowed a mouthful of worms.

1. _____   2. _____

A big bottle of milk.

1. _____   2. _____

Drank it all.

1. _____   2. _____

The monster loves to have worms and milk for a snack.

1. _____   2. _____

Language Arts Skill: Recognizing sentences as complete thoughts

LANGUAGE ARTS

Please State Your Name...
There are different kinds of sentences. One kind is a statement. A **statement** tells about something. A **question** asks something. A question is not a statement. Here are some statements about Trevor.

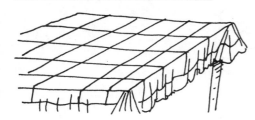

My name is Trevor.
I like toast.
My jacket is orange.
I am perfect.

Statements begin with a capital letter and end with a period. Write **statement** in front of each complete sentence that is a statement. Write **question** in front of each complete sentence that asks a question. If the sentence is not complete, put an **X** in the blank.

_____ Wendell painted his bike bright orange.

_____ Why did he do that?

_____ Wendell lives in an apartment building.

_____ a different school

_____ Do you know Wendell?

_____ Wendell is strange and I like him a lot.

Complete the sentences. Make statements about yourself. Don't forget the period.

I used to be _____

But now I am _____

I used to wear _____

But now I wear _____

I used to say _____

But now I say _____

Language Arts Skill: Identifying and writing statements

LANGUAGE ARTS

Ask Me a Question

Another kind of sentence is called a **question**. Questions ask something. They end with a question mark (**?**). Here are some questions about Ricardo.

Where is Ricardo going?
Who is Ricardo's best friend?
What do you think about Ricardo's hat?
When is Ricardo supposed to go home?
Why does Ricardo have a pet turtle?

Look at these statements. Can you turn them into questions? Don't forget to start with a capital letter and end with a question mark.

Someone was in the house.

_____

The dog has fleas.

_____

Your favorite music is rock and roll.

_____

Jasper has green hair.

_____

The plant will grow taller.

_____

Minnie can turn a cartwheel.

_____

How about this? Play a game of Twenty Questions with someone in your family. One person thinks of a person, place, or thing. The other person asks all the questions. The answers have to be yes or no only!

Language Arts Skill: Identifying and writing questions

LANGUAGE ARTS

When You Care Enough to Say it Loud

Another kind of sentence is the **exclamation**. You use an exclamation when you have strong feelings. Exclamations can show excitement, happiness, sadness, anger, and lots of other emotions. They can be whole sentences or they can be just one word! They start with a capital letter and end with an exclamation point (**!**).

Write an exclamation showing what you would say. Don't forget to start with a capital letter and end with an exclamation point.

You just found one hundred dollars in the street. _____

Someone keeps teasing you about your enormous feet. _____

Someone takes a lot of trouble to do you a favor. _____

Someone just gave you the best gift you ever got. _____

The most embarrassing thing just happened to you. _____

You just won a lifetime supply of your favorite food. _____

An elephant just ran through your bedroom. _____

Your little sister broke your favorite toy. _____

Your grandpa just told you a great secret. _____

How about this? *Get four or five index cards. Think of four or five situations in which people do something nice for you. How can you say thank you? Write an exclamation on each card. Keep the cards to remind you of nice things to say.*

Language Arts Skill: Identifying and writing exclamations

LANGUAGE ARTS

Huh. Huh? Huh!

Gwendolina never stops talking. If she's not making **statements** about what she thinks, she's asking pesky **questions**. If she's not asking pesky questions, she shouting **exclamations** about something or other. Her class tape-recorded 15 seconds of Gwendolina's non-stop chatter. Here's what they recorded:

Howdy! What's new, chickaboo? I've got a great idea. Why don't we all go jump in the mud? I love rainy days! There is nothing better than rain on your face and mud between your toes. Let's go! Why aren't you guys following me? First I'll roll up my pants. Yikes! This mud puddle is very deep. Oh, no! I'm in up to my waist. Will somebody please help me climb out? Yowza! That mud puddle was more than I bargained for.

Read what Gwendolina said again. Underline all the **statements** she made. Circle all the **questions** she asked. Draw a star above each exclamation.

Here's what Gwendolina's classmates had to say to her. Fill in a period (.), question mark (**?**), or exclamation point (**!**) to show whether each sentence is a statement, question, or exclamation.

Yuck ___
Why don't you let anybody else talk ___
I think you have an awful lot to say ___
Quiet already ___
Gwendolina, where are your manners ___
What's a chickaboo ___
You're dripping mud on the floor ___
Can you sing as well as you talk ___
Gross out ___

Language Arts Skill: Using periods, question marks, and exclamation points

SPELLING AND PHONICS

Beginning Sounds

Many words begin with **consonants**. Consonants are all the letters in the alphabet except the vowels a, e, i, o, and u. Look at the pictures below. Say the picture names. What **beginning consonant** sound do you hear? Write the letter for that sound.

___ook

___uppet

___og

___an

___ine

You can make very different words just by changing the beginning consonant sound. Read the words below. Then change the **beginning consonant** to make a new word!

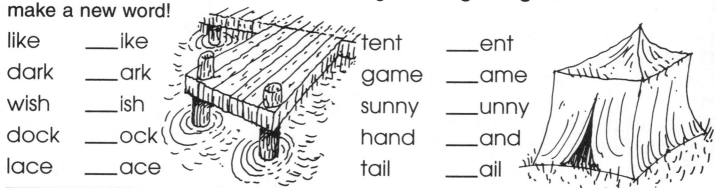

like	___ike		tent	___ent
dark	___ark		game	___ame
wish	___ish		sunny	___unny
dock	___ock		hand	___and
lace	___ace		tail	___ail

Spelling and Phonics Skill: Identifying beginning consonant sounds and letters

SPELLING AND PHONICS

Blast Off with Blends!

Stacy is **bl**asting off into outer **sp**ace. **St**, **bl**, and **sp** are **consonant blends**. You can hear both separate letters when you say the word. Look at the words below. Write in the consonant blends to complete each word.

gr

_____oan

_____umpy

br

_____ing

_____other

cl

_____ap

_____atter

fl

_____y

_____ashlight

dr

_____ip

_____ive

fr

_____ench

_____y

pl

_____ayground

_____anet

str

_____ipes

_____ing

How about this? *Can you circle all the consonant blends in a list of words? You can write your own list! Start your list with* **blue**, **brown**, **clown**, **crown**, **droop**, **frown**, **floor**, **grown-up**, **glue**, **proud**, **plow**, **slow**, **store**, *and* **try**.

Spelling and Phonics Skill: Using and identifying consonant blends

SPELLING AND PHONICS

Squished Sounds

Sometimes two letters come together to make a brand new consonant sound. This is called a **digraph**. For example, the words thick, ship, and chip have the digraphs **th**, **sh**, and **ch**. You do not hear each letter by itself when you say these words.

Finish each word by filling in the letters at the top of the column. Then say the word you completed.

th

_____irteen

_____ud

_____ousand

_____ank

ch

_____eck

_____eese

_____oose

_____ick

sh

_____eep

_____op

_____ine

_____ape

How about this? *Digraphs can appear in the middle or at the end of a word, too. Some examples are* ***wash****,* ***sandwich****, and* ***math****. (Sometimes the* ***ch*** *sound is spelled* ***tch****.) Can you write a list of words with digraphs in the middle or at the end?*

Spelling and Phonics Skill: Using consonant digraphs

SPELLING AND PHONICS

A is for Ant

The vowels **a**, **e**, **i**, **o**, and **u** all have long and short sounds. The long sounds are easy to remember—just say the name of the letter! But it's not so easy to remember the short sounds. The **short sound** for **a** is the sound you hear at the beginning of **ant**. You also hear it in the middle of **bag**.

Write an **a** on the line to complete the word. Say the sound for **short a** and the whole word to yourself as you write.

__pple	__nd	b__t
c__rrot	s__t	b__ckp__ck
__nimal	h__nd	sn__ck
bl__ck	c__t	s__ndwich
c__n	cl__pped	m__p

Write a word from above for each picture.

_____   _____   _____

Write two sentences using words from the list above.

_____

_____

_____

Spelling and Phonics Skill: Identifying the sound for short a

SPELLING AND PHONICS

E is for Elf

The **short sound** for **e** is the sound you hear at the beginning of **elf**. You also hear it in the middle of **wet**.

Write an **e** on the line to complete the word. Say the sound for **short e** and the whole word to yourself as you write.

__very	__dge	__gg
__nter	__cho	__lephant
b__d	f__d	s__t
m__t	sl__d	n__ver
__nvelope	l__tter	p__ncil

Write a word from above for each picture.

_____   _____   _____

Write two sentences using words from the list above.

_____

_____

How about this? *Here's a problem. The letters **ea** can stand for the short sound of **e** also. For example, read the words **bread** and **head**. When you read one of these words, pay attention!*

Spelling and Phonics Skill: Identifying the sound for short e

SPELLING AND PHONICS

Am I an Iguana?

The **short sound** for **i** is the sound you hear at the beginning of **iguana**. It is also at the beginning of **ick**. You hear it in the middle of **fish**. For that matter, it is also in the middle of **middle**!

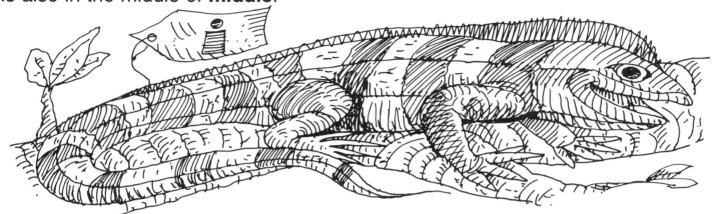

Write an **i** on the line to complete the word. Say the sound for **short i** and the whole word to yourself as you write.

_n	_t	_mprove
_nteresting	b_g	h_dden
s_x	m_lk	m_ttens
w_sh	st_ll	th_n
t_ckle	w_ggle	st_cks

Write a word from above for each picture.

_____   _____   _____

Write two sentences using words from the list above.

_____

_____

Spelling and Phonics Skill: Identifying the sound for short i

SPELLING AND PHONICS

O Is for Octopus

The **short sound** for **o** is the sound you hear at the beginning of **octopus**. You also hear it in the middle of **rock**.

Write an **o** on the line to complete the word. Say the sound for **short o** and the whole word to yourself as you write.

__ctopus	__n	__ften
__ffer	__strich	__pportunity
b__x	d__g	g__ne
s__ck	l__ck	cl__ck
r__cket	tick-t__ck	s__ccer

Write a word from above for each picture.

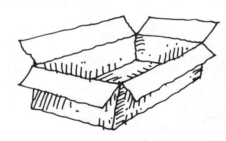

_____ _____ _____

Write two sentences using words from the list above.

_____

_____

Spelling and Phonics Skill: Identifying the sound for short o

SPELLING AND PHONICS

Put Up That Umbrella!
The **short sound** for **u** is the sound you hear at the beginning of **umbrella** and **up**. You also hear it in the middle of **duck**.

Write a **u** on the line to complete the word. Say the sound for **short u** and the whole word to yourself as you write.

__p	__nder	__ntil
__mbrella	__ncle	__gly
b__s	t__b	b__g
r__n	f__n	dr__m
th__nder	m__scle	r__mble

Write a word from above for each picture.

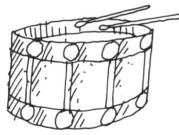  

_____ _____ _____

Write two sentences using words from the list above.

_____

_____

Spelling and Phonics Skill: Identifying the sound for short u

SPELLING AND PHONICS

Invisible Vowels

Katrina likes to write **a**, **e**, **i**, **o**, and **u** in invisible ink! In the words below, some of the vowels have vanished. You will have to write them in if you want to read Katrina's list of words.

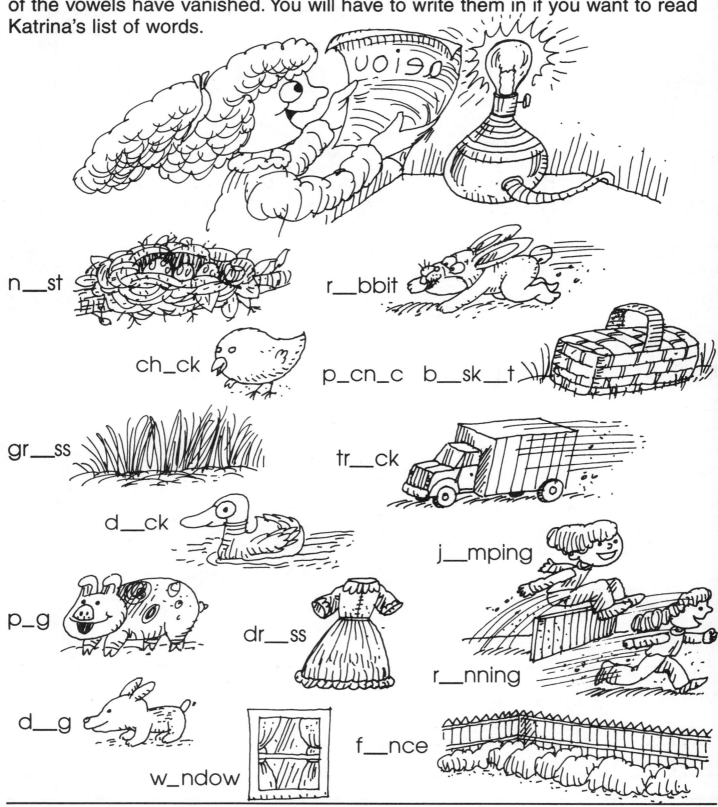

n__st

r__bbit

ch_ck

p_cn_c   b__sk__t

gr__ss

tr__ck

d__ck

j__mping

p_g

dr__ss

r__nning

d_g

w_ndow

f__nce

Spelling and Phonics Skill: Distinguishing short vowel sounds

SPELLING AND PHONICS

Long Vowels

Long vowels say their own names. Listen for them in these words.

long a in rake
long e in bee
long i in kite
long o in boat
long u in cube

Say the picture names and circle the word that has a long vowel sound.

| hat   cake | tree   net | fish   bike |
| coat   frog | sun   mule | dime   six |

Read these words. Circle the words with a long vowel sound.

| skip | game | not | wet | tune |
| slide | sand | note | beet | fun |

Spelling and Phonics Skill: Distinguishing long vowel sounds

SPELLING AND PHONICS

The Long and Short of It

Read the sentence. Then read the two words below it. One has a short vowel sound. They other has a long vowel sound. Write the word that makes sense on the line. If it has a short vowel sound, circle it.

Some people say I act in a very _____ way.
odd   old

What do they _____?
knob   know

I like to eat ketchup on my _____.
cake   cat

I dress up like a _____ when it isn't even Halloween.
witch   wide

I act in a normal way _____ of the time.
mop   most

But I don't even _____ when people say I'm weird.
kite   blink

I like to _____ a fort with tin cans, get inside, and knock the fort over.
bike   build

I have about a _____ ideas for having fun.
miles   million

Spelling and Phonics Skill: Writing words with short and long vowel sounds

SPELLING AND PHONICS

Vowels Make Me Howl

José is learning about the funny tricks vowels can play. Sometimes words that look like they should rhyme actually don't! Look at the words below. They all end in **–ove**. But there are lots of different ways to pronounce them. Look at the chart to figure out how each of these words should be said. Say the word, and then write it.

sounds like **uh-v**	sounds like **oo-v**	sounds like **oh-v**
love	move	stove
above	prove	drove

How about this? There are lots of tricky words that look like they should rhyme, but don't. Think about word pairs like **new** and **sew**, or like **heard** and **beard**. Can you think of any others?

Spelling and Phonics Skill: Recognizing irregular vowel sounds and spellings

SPELLING AND PHONICS

Freak-Out Week

This week, Pete and Sandeep and Jeanie are learning about different ways to spell the same vowel sounds. Their names all have the **long e** sound, but each of them spells it a different way! Pete spells it **ete**, Sandeep spells it **eep**, and Jeanie spells it **ean**. Can you find other words that rhyme even though they are spelled differently?

Look in the word box below. Find a pair of rhyming words to complete each rhyme. Write the words in the blanks. Do the same on the next page, too!

When I can't do something, I moan and I _____,
but I never or hardly ever really ____.

One day at the beach, I looked in my _____.
Swimming in there was a baby blue _____!

My teacher thinks I'm really _____,
because my homework is never _____.

I took some yarn and look what I _____.
To clip to my head, a long yellow _____!

whale	braid	sigh	great
pail	made	cry	late

Spelling and Phonics Skill: Recognizing irregular vowel sounds and spellings

SPELLING AND PHONICS

wool home known roll
full comb bone bowl

My hair is a mess cause I just left my _____

with a ball and a bat but not with my _____.

The pancakes you made tasted like _____,

but I'll tell you instead that I'm really _____.

First I'll have some juice and a _____,

then cereal crackling in my _____.

If only, if only, if only I'd _____

you just got a dog! I'd have brought you a _____.

Now you write a two-line verse. Try to use two rhyming words that have different spellings.

_____

_____

How about this? *Why not write a two-line rhyme for someone at home? No special occasion—just a rhyme to make him or her feel good.*

Spelling and Phonics Skill: Recognizing irregular vowel sounds and spellings

SPELLING AND PHONICS

One L–L–L–Lump or Two?

Some people like one lump of sugar in their tea. Other people like two lumps. Words can be just as weird as people. Some words need one **l**, while other words need two.

Read these sentences. Write **l** or **ll** in each unfinished word. You can look at the word list for help.

I get home at 3:00 from schoo__.

I a__ways change my clothes.

Then I ca__ my dad at work.

I say he__o, and he says hi.

We ta__k for about five minutes.

If I remember, I bring in the mai__.

After that, I have a sma__ snack.

I make a cup of tea and mi__k.

Sometimes, I fa__ asleep while I'm doing my homework.

I always doze off if my homework is spe__ing.

After that, I draw a picture with cha __k.

We have a bulletin board that hangs on the wa__.

It is in a long, narrow ha__.

Then I go outside to play ba__.

talk	mail	hello	call	milk	always	hall	wall
ball	small	chalk	spelling	fall	school		

How about this? *There are lots of words that have double consonants. Some of these words are **narrow, letter, sizzle,** and **offer**. Why not look in a magazine or a newspaper for other words that have double consonants in them? Circle all the words you find.*

Spelling and Phonics Skill: Understanding double consonants

SPELLING AND PHONICS

A Letter that Makes No Sound

Lots of words end with a **silent e**. Just because the silent e doesn't make any sound, that doesn't mean it's not doing anything! The silent e changes other vowels from short to long. Look at the words **can** and **cane**. Listen to the **short a** sound in can. But when you add the silent e, the word changes to cane with a **long a** sound.

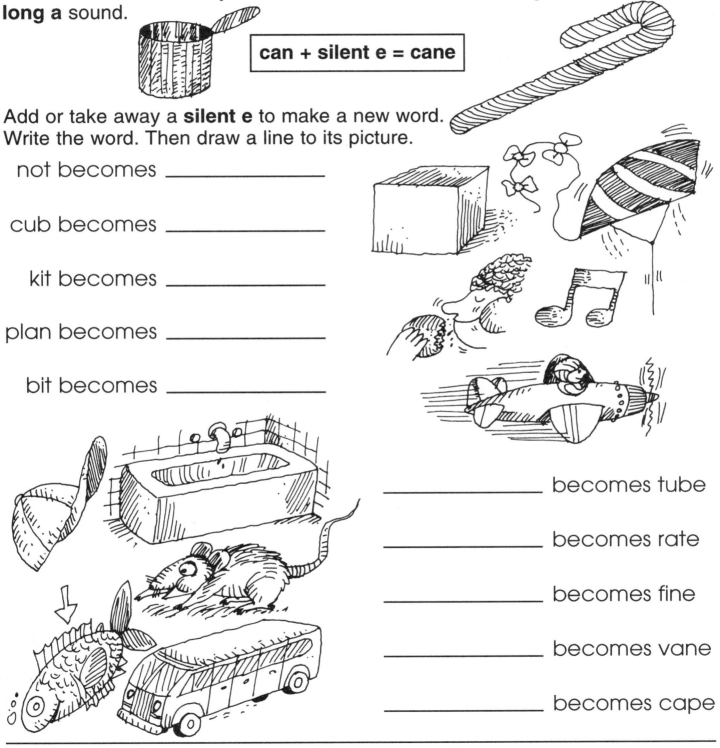

can + silent e = cane

Add or take away a **silent e** to make a new word. Write the word. Then draw a line to its picture.

not becomes _____

cub becomes _____

kit becomes _____

plan becomes _____

bit becomes _____

_____ becomes tube

_____ becomes rate

_____ becomes fine

_____ becomes vane

_____ becomes cape

Spelling and Phonics Skill: Identifying long vowels with silent e

SPELLING AND PHONICS

More Silent Letters

There are a lot of letters that can be silent. Each of these words has a silent letter missing. Sound it out and read it out loud. Then fill in the missing silent letter. Then read the word out loud again. It should sound exactly the same!

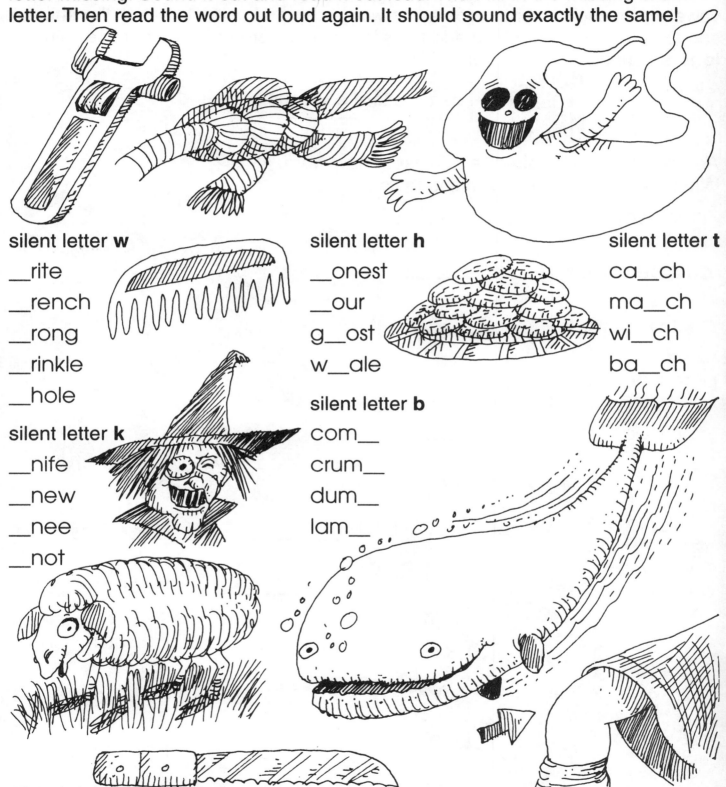

silent letter w

__rite

__rench

__rong

__rinkle

__hole

silent letter k

__nife

__new

__nee

__not

silent letter h

__onest

__our

g__ost

w__ale

silent letter b

com__

crum__

dum__

lam__

silent letter t

ca__ch

ma__ch

wi__ch

ba__ch

Spelling and Phonics Skill: Recognizing silent letters

226

SPELLING AND PHONICS

Funny, Phunny, Ghunny? Laff, Laph, Laugh?
Oh, no! Will the tricks never end? Sometimes you say a word with an **f sound** but there is not an **f** in sight. Sometimes **ph** makes the **f sound**. Other times, **gh** makes the **f sound**.

ele**ph**ant **f**antastic cou**gh** lau**gh** tele**ph**one **ph**onics dol**ph**in enou**gh** tou**gh** **f**ish al**ph**abet rou**gh** **f**un

Use the list to complete the sentences with words that have an **f** sound. As you write each word, say the **f** sound and then say the whole word.

I was sitting in my front yard talking on my cell _____.

A huge, gray _____ came walking down the street.

I tried not to _____ or giggle when he said, "I've lost my circus."

"That's too bad," I said. "That's really _____ luck."

Then he began to sneeze and _____.

"If you hold your breath long _____, you will stop sneezing," I said.

"To stop sneezing I usually say the _____ backwards starting
   with Z," he said.

"You seem to know a lot about letters, vowels, and other _____,"
   I said.

"Yes," he said. "My friend, the swimming _____, taught me."

"That sounds like one _____ fish!" I exclaimed.

"Actually, a dolphin is not a ____," he corrected me.

"I like you," said the elephant. "If I promise not to play too _____,
   can I move in with you?"

"Why not?" I said. "I would like that very much. My mom likes me to
   have as much ____ as possible."

Spelling and Phonics Skill: Using gh and ph to spell the consonant sound of f

227

SPELLING AND PHONICS

Silent Night

The letters **gh** are very tricky. They can spell the **f sound** in **laugh**. They can also be silent, as in the words **sigh** and **daughter**. Look at the word list below for some examples of words using a **silent gh**. Can you find and circle those words in the word find below?

night
sigh
right
knight
taught
daughter
naughty
though

n	i	g	h	t	t	e	c	r
m	k	o	i	h	r	c	x	i
k	u	a	g	g	w	v	d	g
z	j	i	k	i	q	u	a	h
s	n	h	v	s	w	r	u	t
k	a	s	r	n	t	f	g	p
c	u	f	t	a	u	g	h	t
i	g	d	l	g	h	p	t	n
t	h	g	i	n	k	o	e	d
l	t	h	o	c	w	s	r	h
a	y	g	j	m	h	q	x	i
r	t	h	o	u	g	h	e	p

Spelling and Phonics Skill: Recognizing silent gh

SPELLING AND PHONICS

More! More! More!

Mom gives Todd something special every day. But Todd is never happy with just one thing. He wants more and more. To show that a noun means more than one, Todd knows to add an **–s**. This is called making it **plural**. Look at the list of things Mom gave Todd. Then rewrite the list to make everything plural. The first one has been done for you.

comb **+ s = combs**   horse _____

camera _____   lion _____

note _____   chimpanzee _____

crayon _____   newspaper _____

flower _____   onion _____

feather _____   flute _____

frog _____   skateboard _____

elephant _____ peanut _____

orange _____   sailboat _____

rabbit _____   truck _____

ladder _____

Spelling and Phonics Skill: Creating plural nouns by adding –s

SPELLING AND PHONICS

It's Easy with –ES

Richie Rex has a lunchbo**x**, a di**sh**, a sandwi**ch**, and a gla**ss**. He has one of everything. But here comes Cherry Essex! What will Richie Rex do? He needs to make plurals of everything. There is a special way to make plurals for nouns that end in **x**, **sh**, **ch**, and **ss**. Instead of adding –s, Richie Rex needs to add –**es**.

lunchbox + **es** = lunchboxes
sandwich + **es** = sandwiches
dish + **es** = dishes
glass + **es** = glasses

Look at the nouns in bold. Circle the word that shows how to make that noun mean more than one.

class	classs	classes	**peach**	peachs	peaches
beach	beaches	beachs	**dress**	dresses	dreses
fox	foxses	foxes	**match**	matchs	matches
kiss	kises	kisses	**fax**	faxes	faxs
ax	axes	axs	**mess**	messs	messes
brush	brushes	brushs			

Spelling and Phonics Skill: Creating plural nouns by adding –es

SPELLING AND PHONICS

Why Oh Y?

Tony and Tommy hate to share. They fight all the time. Tony says that Tommy is a real baby. Tommy says Tony is a real baby. Mom and Dad say they are both babies. To make a noun that ends in –**y** plural, you must change the **y** to an **i**, and then add –**es**.

baby → babi + es → babies

Tommy and Tony made lots of mistakes when they made their list of plurals. Can you fix them? Start with the list of things that end in –**y**. Cross out the **y** and change it to **i**. Then add –**es**. Then spell out the whole word on the blank.

A LIST By Tony and Tommy	
candys	candy _____
puppis	puppy _____
penies	penny _____
hankys	hanky _____
skis	sky _____
french frys	french fry _____
butterflis	butterfly _____
good tryes	good try _____
kittys	kitty _____

Spelling and Phonics Skill: Creating plural nouns by adding –ies to words ending in –y

SPELLING AND PHONICS

Weirder and Weirder

Some nouns break all the rules! Adding an **–s** won't make them plural. Adding an **–es** won't make them plural. Even adding an **–ies** won't do it! To make them plural, you have to change their whole spelling.

| mice | leaves | teeth | women | men |
| children | feet | geese | hooves |

These nouns need special attention to make them mean more than one. Look at the plurals in the word box. Can you find the plural for each noun? Write it on the blank.

One	More Than One
woman	_____
man	_____
child	_____
foot	_____
tooth	_____
mouse	_____
goose	_____
leaf	_____
hoof	_____

Spelling and Phonics Skill: Irregular plural nouns

SPELLING AND PHONICS

I Remember When

Verbs tell about things that are happening. But Mrs. Marcy Proost wants to talk about things that happened yesterday, last week, and last year. What can she do? To make a verb tell what happened in the past, she can add –**d** or –**ed**.

jump + ed = jumped
chase + d = chased
walk + ed = walked

Read Mrs. Marcy Proost's story below. Look at the underlined verbs. Can you change them to make them explain something in the past? If the verb ends in the letter **e**, add a **d** to make it past tense. If the verb does not end in the letter **e**, add **ed** to make it past tense.

When I was a little girl, I <u>taste</u> some delicious cookies. I <u>wiggle</u> and <u>move</u> around while I ate them. Sadly, I <u>spill</u> some milk on my dress. My mother <u>decide</u> we should wash the dress. We <u>enter</u> the laundry room. Then we <u>load</u> the washer. We <u>add</u> some laundry detergent. Then we <u>close</u> the washer door. The machine <u>whine</u> when we <u>turn</u> it on. Mom and I <u>play</u> a game of hopscotch and <u>bake</u> some more cookies for a while. Then we put the clothes in the dryer. Soon, they were ready! We <u>fold</u> them up. Then we <u>share</u> some more cookies and milk. The funny thing is, this time Mom <u>spill</u> milk on herself!

How about this? Write a paragraph about what you did today. Did you use any verbs that end in d or ed? Circle them!

Spelling and Phonics Skill: Adding –d and –ed to verbs in the past tense

SPELLING AND PHONICS

Double Trouble

Some past tense verbs have tricky spellings. You can't just add –**ed**! Instead, you have to double the consonant at the end of the word. Then you can add –**ed**. This usually happens when the verb has a short vowel sound and ends in a single consonant.

tug ⟶ tugg ⟶ tugged
zap ⟶ zapp ⟶ zapped

Make these verbs past tense. First double the consonant at the end of the word, and then add –**ed**.

hug	stir	clap	grab
_____	_____	_____	_____
plan	brag	skip	trip
_____	_____	_____	_____
nap	wrap	chat	bat
_____	_____	_____	_____
beg	hop	stop	drop
_____	_____	_____	_____

How about this? *You can use the same rule when you are adding –ing to a verb. If the verb has a short vowel sound and ends in a single consonant, double the consonant before you add –ing. For example, **tugging** and **zapping**. Why not write a list showing all the verbs above with –ing?*

Spelling and Phonics Skill: Doubling the final consonant before adding –ed or –ing

SPELLING AND PHONICS

A Nerdy Bird

While Arthur was eating some sherbet, his nerdy bird Earl tore up Arthur's homework! The homework was writing down words that have the sound **er**. The **er** sound can be spelled lots of different ways: **ir**, **ur**, and **ear**, for example. Arthur had listed the words he found by how they are spelled.

blur   burp   curl   girl   nervous   learn

burger

chirp   hurt   her   fur   nerd

purr   sir

er   **ur**

_____   _____
_____   _____
_____   _____
_____   _____
_____   _____
_____   _____

ir   **ear**
_____
_____   _____
_____   _____
_____   _____
_____   _____
                       _____

verb   earn   squirrel   serve   heard   pearl

search   third   shirt

One word belongs in two different lists. Write it here! _____

How about this? *There is a word that uses **or** to spell the **er** sound. How bizarre! Can you guess what it is? Here is a hint: you can find the word in this sentence!*

Spelling and Phonics Skill: Spelling the er sound with different vowel combinations

SPELLING AND PHONICS

<u>Si</u><u>ck</u> <u>Ch</u>ris and the <u>K</u>ind Do<u>c</u>tor

There are lots of different ways to spell the **k** sound. It can be spelled with a **c**, **k**, **ck**, or **ch**. Read the list of words with **k** sounds. Then read the story. Fill in the blanks with **c**, **k**, **ck**, or **ch** to spell each word correctly.

ache backpack block camera Christmas comb cool cost crowd cutie deck doctor escape jacket kangaroo keep key kind kiss make market neck nickel pack pocket poke school sick skin stomach took walk

After the holiday party at <u>s   ool</u>, I started to feel a little <u>si   </u>. Nothing major: just a belly <u>a   e</u>. I try to look <u>   ool</u>, so I took my <u>   omb</u> out of my <u>po   et</u> to fix my hair before I said, "Dudes, I'm going to <u>ma   e</u> my <u>es   ape</u>. It's time for me to see the <u>do   tor</u>." (You see, my Mom is a doctor!) Then I grabbed my <u>ba   pa   </u> and ran out the door.

I live just one <u>blo   </u> away, so I <u>wal   ed</u> home. I opened the front door with my <u>   ey</u>. Soon, Mom was home from the <u>mar   et</u>. "Hi, <u>   utie</u>," she said. She gave me a big <u>   iss</u>. Then she felt how hot my <u>s   in</u> was, and listened to my <u>stoma   </u>. Mom is so <u>   ind</u>!

"I'll bet a <u>ni   el</u> I know what the problem is," she said. "Too many <u>   ristmas</u> cookies!"

How about this? *The letter combination* **qu** *makes the sound* **kw**. *What words do you see if you add* **qu** *to* –**ack**, –**ick**, –**it**, –**ite**, *and* –**een**?

Spelling and Phonics Skill: Using c, k, ck, ch, and qu to spell the k sound

SPELLING AND PHONICS

It's Rhyme Time

The Stine brothers, Roger and Hammer, are writing songs. They need lots of rhyming words. But rhyming sounds aren't always spelled the same way. Look at the words they've found. Draw lines to connect the words that rhyme, even though they are spelled in very different ways.

pull	thought
boat	wool
hope	made
caught	wrote
raid	home
comb	soap
bone	roll
try	trees
bowl	sigh
seize	late
great	known
pail	week
beak	whale

How about this? Can you think of other words that rhyme with the words on this page? Can you write a rhyming song using some of them?

Spelling and Phonics Skill: Recognizing alternate spellings of rhyming sounds

CURSIVE WRITING

Love That Lowercase

Cursive writing is wild and crazy! Look at the lowercase alphabet in cursive. Trace each letter. Next to it, write the letter again, by yourself. Now you can look at this page whenever you get stumped writing lowercase cursive letters!

a   b   c   d

e   f   g   h

i   j   k   l

m   n   o

p   q   r   s

t   u   v   w

x   y   z

Cursive Writing Skill: Tracing and writing lowercase cursive letters

CURSIVE WRITING

A Matching Mess

Look at the mess of lowercase letters below. Some are printed and some are cursive. Draw lines to match the printed letters with their cursive versions.

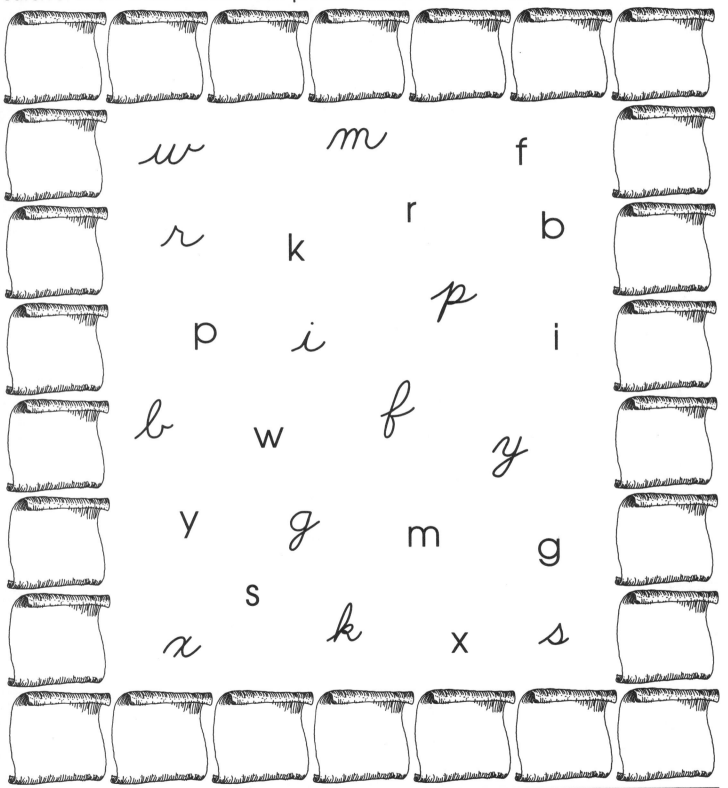

Cursive Writing Skill: Identifying cursive and printed lowercase letter pairs

CURSIVE WRITING

The Case of the Uppercase

Look at the uppercase letters in the cursive alphabet. They are also called **capitals**. Trace each letter. Next to it, write the letter again, by yourself. You never know when this page will come in handy. You can look at it whenever you forget how to write an uppercase cursive letter!

Cursive Writing Skill: Tracing and writing uppercase cursive letters

CURSIVE WRITING

A Capital Catastrophe

What a disaster! The uppercase letters below are all mixed up. Some are printed and some are cursive. Draw lines to match the printed letters with their cursive versions.

Cursive Writing Skill: Identifying cursive and printed uppercase letter pairs

CURSIVE WRITING

Aa and Bb

Anna and Bobby are feeding an ape and a bear. **Anna** and **ape** start with **A** and **a**. **Bobby** and **bear** start with **B** and **b**. Practice tracing and writing **Aa** and **Bb** in cursive below. Then practice some words that feature these letters.

a   a   a   a

a   a   a   a

Anna

ape

B   B   B   B

b   b   b   b

Bobby

bear

The bear wears a bib to eat an apple. Can you write **apple** and **bib** in cursive? Write any other **A** and **B** words you can think of.

Cursive Writing Skill: Writing uppercase and lowercase cursive letters A and B

CURSIVE WRITING

Cc and Dd

Carlos and Daria are pretending to drive a car. **Carlos** and **car** start with **C** and **c**. **Daria** and **drive** start with **D** and **d**. Practice tracing and writing **Cc** and **Dd** in cursive below. Then practice some words that feature these letters.

calm down!

C C C C C

c c c c c

Carlos

can

D D D D

d d d d

Daria

drive

Carlos is telling Daria to calm down! Can you write **calm** and **down** in cursive? Write any other **C** and **D** words you can think of.

Cursive Writing Skill: Writing uppercase and lowercase cursive letters C and D

CURSIVE WRITING

$\mathcal{E}e$ and $\mathcal{F}f$

Ella and Fitzer end the race at the finish line. **Ella** and **end** start with **E** and **e**. **Fitzer** and **finish** start with **F** and **f**. Practice tracing and writing **Ee** and **Ff** in cursive below. Then practice some words that feature these letters.

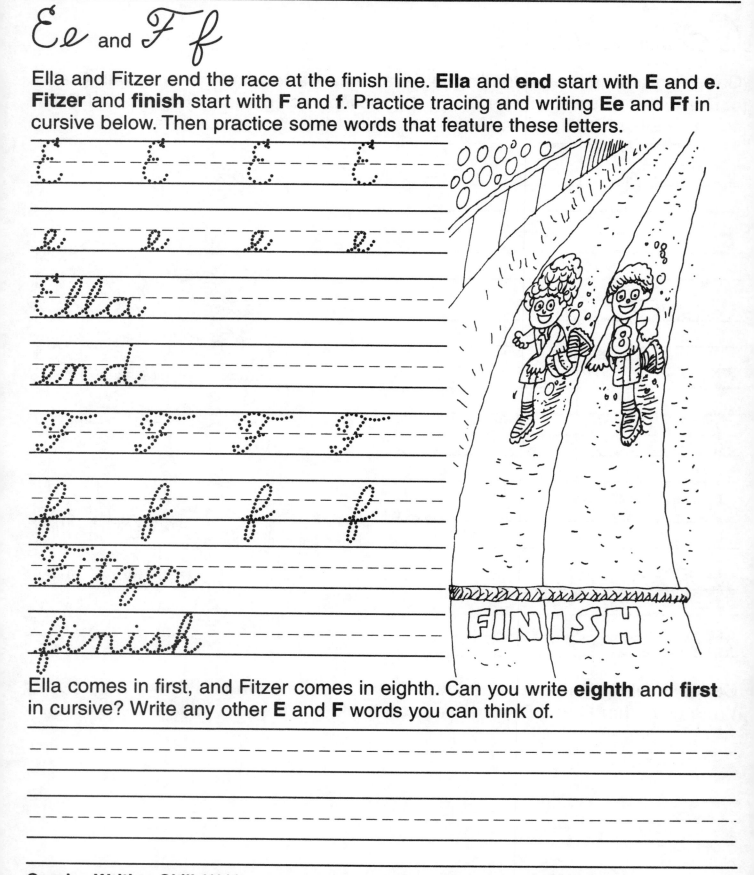

E   E   E   E

e   e   e   e

Ella

end

F   F   F   F

f   f   f   f

Fitzer

finish

Ella comes in first, and Fitzer comes in eighth. Can you write **eighth** and **first** in cursive? Write any other **E** and **F** words you can think of.

Cursive Writing Skill: Writing uppercase and lowercase cursive letters E and F

CURSIVE WRITING

$\mathscr{G}g$ and $\mathscr{H}h$

Gert and Hildy are going head to head. **Gert** and **going** start with **G** and **g**. **Hildy** and **head** start with **H** and **h**. Practice tracing and writing **Gg** and **Hh** in cursive below. Then practice some words that feature these letters.

Gert says "Oh, golly!" Hildy says "Oh, help!" Can you write **golly** and **help** in cursive? Write any other **G** and **H** words you can think of.

Cursive Writing Skill: Writing uppercase and lowercase cursive letters G and H

CURSIVE WRITING

I i and *J j*

Izzie and Joe are jumping into the lake. **Izzie** and **into** start with **I** and **i**. **Joe** and **jump** start with **J** and **j**. Practice tracing and writing **Ii** and **Jj** in cursive below. Then practice some words that feature these letters.

I   I   I   I

i   i   i   i

Izzie

into

J   J   J   J

j   j   j   j

Joe

jump

Izzie dropped his ice cream. Joe is losing his jellybeans. Can you write **ice cream** and **jellybeans** in cursive? Write any other **I** and **J** words you can think of.

Cursive Writing Skill: Writing uppercase and lowercase cursive letters I and J

CURSIVE WRITING

Kk and *Ll*

Kiki and Lila keep the light on. **Kiki** and **keep** start with **K** and **k**. **Lila** and **light** start with **L** and **l**. Practice tracing and writing **Kk** and **Ll** in cursive below. Then practice some words that feature these letters.

Kiki and Lila love their kittens. Can you write **kitten** and **love** in cursive? Write any other **K** and **L** words you can think of.

Cursive Writing Skill: Writing uppercase and lowercase cursive letters K and L

CURSIVE WRITING

$\mathcal{Mm}$ and $\mathcal{Nn}$

Mutto is messy and Nutto is neat. **Mutto** and **messy** start with **M** and **m**. **Nutto** and **neat** start with **N** and **n**. Practice tracing and writing **Mm** and **Nn** in cursive below. Then practice some words that feature these letters.

$\mathcal{M} \quad \mathcal{M} \quad \mathcal{M} \quad \mathcal{M}$

$\mathcal{m} \quad \mathcal{m} \quad \mathcal{m} \quad \mathcal{m}$

$\mathcal{Mutto}$

$\mathcal{messy}$

$\mathcal{N} \quad \mathcal{N} \quad \mathcal{N} \quad \mathcal{N}$

$\mathcal{n} \quad \mathcal{n} \quad \mathcal{n} \quad \mathcal{n}$

$\mathcal{Nutto}$

$\mathcal{neat}$

Mutto and Nutto both like to drink a nice glass of milk. Can you write **milk** and **nice** in cursive? Write any other **M** and **N** words you can think of.

Cursive Writing Skill: Writing uppercase and lowercase cursive letters M and N

CURSIVE WRITING

Oo and *Pp*

Ollie and Pop like to open presents. **Ollie** and **open** start with **O** and **o**. **Pop** and **presents** start with **P** and **p**. Practice tracing and writing **Oo** and **Pp** in cursive below. Then practice some words that feature these letters.

O   O   O   O

o   o   o   o

Ollie

open

P   P   P   P

p   p   p   p

Pop

present

Strange presents! The boxes are full of onions and pickles! Can you write **onions** and **pickles** in cursive? Write any other **O** and **P** words you can think of.

Cursive Writing Skill: Writing uppercase and lowercase cursive letters O and P

CURSIVE WRITING

Qq and *Rr*

Queen Rumba decided to quit the race! **Queen** and **quit** start with **Q** and **q**. **Rumba** and **race** start with **R** and **r**. Practice tracing and writing **Qq** and **Rr** in cursive below. Then practice some words that feature these letters.

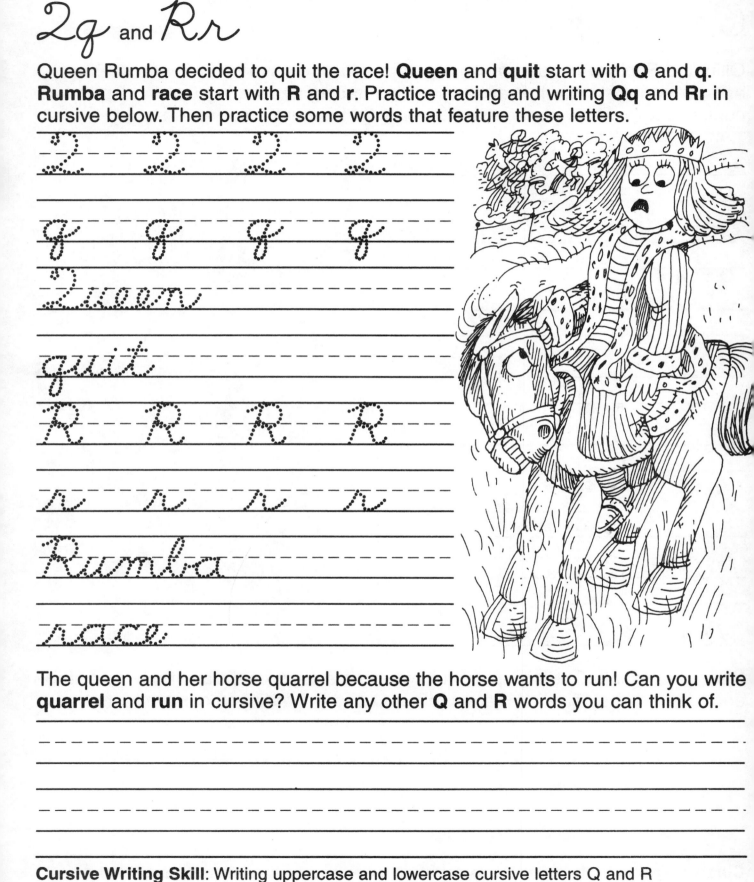

Q Q Q Q

q q q q

Queen

quit

R R R R

r r r r

Rumba

race

The queen and her horse quarrel because the horse wants to run! Can you write **quarrel** and **run** in cursive? Write any other **Q** and **R** words you can think of.

Cursive Writing Skill: Writing uppercase and lowercase cursive letters Q and R

CURSIVE WRITING

Ss and Tt

Stan and Terp sit and talk. **Stan** and **sit** start with **S** and **s**. **Terp** and **talk** start with **T** and **t**. Practice tracing and writing **Ss** and **Tt** in cursive below. Then practice some words that feature these letters.

S   S   S   S

s   s   s   s

Stan

sit

T   T   T   T

t   t   t   t

Terp

talk

Stan and Terp go inside when it starts to thunder. Can you write **start** and **thunder** in cursive? Write any other **S** and **T** words you can think of.

Cursive Writing Skill: Writing uppercase and lowercase cursive letters S and T

CURSIVE WRITING

𝒰𝓊 and 𝒱𝓋

Uncle Vanya sits under his vine. **Uncle** and **under** start with **U** and **u**. **Vanya** and **vine** start with **V** and **v**. Practice tracing and writing **Uu** and **Vv** in cursive below. Then practice some words that feature these letters.

𝒰 𝒰 𝒰 𝒰

𝓊 𝓊 𝓊 𝓊

𝒰𝓃𝒸𝓁𝑒

𝓊𝓃𝒹𝑒𝓇

𝒱 𝒱 𝒱 𝒱

𝓋 𝓋 𝓋 𝓋

𝒱𝒶𝓃𝓎𝒶

𝓋𝒾𝓃𝑒

Uncle Vanya buttons up his vest. Can you write **up** and **vest** in cursive? Write any other **U** and **V** words you can think of.

Cursive Writing Skill: Writing uppercase and lowercase cursive letters U and V

CURSIVE WRITING

$\mathcal{Ww}$ and $\mathcal{Xx}$

Wally Xero works on an x-ray. **Wally** and **works** start with **W** and **w**. **Xero** and **x-ray** start with **X** and **x**. Practice tracing and writing **Ww** and **Xx** in cursive below. Then practice some words that feature these letters.

$\mathcal{W}$ $\mathcal{W}$ $\mathcal{W}$ $\mathcal{W}$

w w w w

$\mathcal{Wally}$

$works$

$\mathcal{X}$ $\mathcal{X}$ $\mathcal{X}$ $\mathcal{X}$

x x x x

$\mathcal{Xero}$

$x\text{-}ray$

Wally wishes he were playing the xylophone. Can you write **wishes** and **xylophone** in cursive? Write any other **W** and **X** words you can think of.

Cursive Writing Skill: Writing uppercase and lowercase cursive letters W and X

CURSIVE WRITING

Yy and *Zz*

Yadja and Zuzu see a zebra in the yard! **Yadja** and **yard** start with **Y** and **y**. **Zuzu** and **zebra** start with **Z** and **z**. Practice tracing and writing **Yy** and **Zz** in cursive below. Then practice some words that feature these letters.

Y   Y   Y   Y

Y   Y   Y   Y

Yadja

yard

Z   Z   Z   Z

Z   Z   Z   Z

Zuzu

zebra

Yadja and Zuzu yawn when they see a zebra in the zoo. Can you write **yawn** and **zoo** in cursive? Write any other **Y** and **Z** words you can think of.

_____

_____

_____

_____

Cursive Writing Skill: Writing uppercase and lowercase cursive letters Y and Z

CURSIVE WRITING

Putting It All Together

This is one confused alphabet book. Can you draw lines to connect the uppercase letters with the matching lowercase letters?

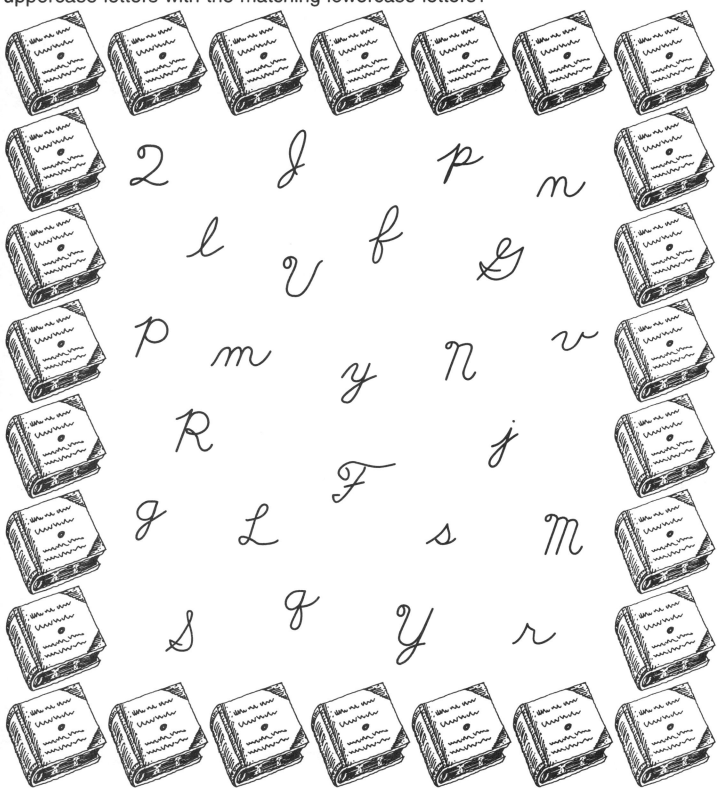

Cursive Writing Skill: Identifying uppercase and lowercase cursive letter pairs

CURSIVE WRITING

Lookalike Letters: a/d and o/c

Sometimes different cursive letters have similar shapes in them. That makes them easier to learn—but harder to tell apart! See how **a** and **d** are the same. See how **o** and **c** are the same. Think about what your hand does differently when you write them. Practice writing **a**, **d**, **o**, and **c**. Then try some words that use them.

dad

added

darts

and

made

Dan

mad

on

the

dock

Rocky

caught

some

codfish

Cursive Writing Skill: Distinguishing lowercase cursive letters with similar forms

CURSIVE WRITING

Losing My Mind Over Letters: f/j/p and g/q
Some cursive letters drop below the writing line! It's important to look closely at these letters! See how **f** and **j** and **p** are the same. See how **g** and **q** are the same. Think about what your hand does differently when you write them. Practice writing **f**, **j**, **p**, **g**, and **q**. Then try some words that use them.

flapjack

fun

piffle

jump

flip

fig

juggle

quark

quip

gumbo

gunk

guppy

piggy

pogo stick

Cursive Writing Skill: Distinguishing lowercase cursive letters with similar forms

CURSIVE WRITING

Cursive Catastrophes: m/n and i/t

Oh no! These letter pairs are almost exactly the same! See how **m** and **n** are the same. See how **i** and **t** are the same. Think about what your hand does differently when you write them. Practice writing **m**, **n**, **i**, and **t**. Then try some words that use them.

man

money

ninny

number

manta

mama

minty

it

tie

tilt

tinted

into

timid

hit

Cursive Writing Skill: Distinguishing lowercase cursive letters with similar forms

CURSIVE WRITING

Looping Lookalikes: l/b/h/k
Some cursive letters have loops that go high up to the top of your writing line!
But each letter is a little different. Look at these letters, and think about what is
the same and what is different about them. Think about what your hand does
differently when you write them. Practice writing **l**, **b**, **h**, and **k**. Then try some
words that use them.

look

laboratory

bah

humbug

chalk

hokey

black

back

hold

chock

clock

block

balk

lucky

Cursive Writing Skill: Distinguishing lowercase cursive letters with similar forms

259

CURSIVE WRITING

Cursive Confusion: r/s and u/v/w

Even simple cursive letters can get mixed up. See how **r** and **s** are the same. See how **u** and **v** and **w** are the same. Think about what your hand does differently when you write them. Practice writing **r**, **s**, **u**, **v**, and **w**. Then try some words that use them.

rust

star

sore

rush

straw

sorry

Mars

wow

over

wonder

uncle

wives

vulture

wave

Cursive Writing Skill: Distinguishing lowercase cursive letters with similar forms

CURSIVE WRITING

Same and Different: y/z and e/x

Some cursive letters are almost the same. Other letters are not. See how **y** and **z** are the same. See how **e** and **x** have nothing in common. Think about what your hand does differently when you write them. Practice writing **y**, **z**, **e**, and **x**. Then try some words that use them.

eyes

zinnia

expect

yearly

zany

zigzag

zesty

extra

oxen

sixteen

excited

yippy-i-yay!

T.Rex

Texas

Cursive Writing Skill: Distinguishing lowercase cursive letters with similar forms

CURSIVE WRITING

Uppercase Confusion: R/B/D and F/T

Uppercase cursive letters can look alike. See how **R**, **B**, and **D** are the same. See how **F** and **T** are the same. Think about what your hand does differently when you write them. Practice writing **R**, **B**, **D**, **F**, and **T**. Then write some sentences that use them.

Bob Roberts went to Doctor Biggan Robust on Dirty Bug Drive in Recoverville.

Felix Talcum from Tours, France, visited Tabby Frimm in Forest Town on Tuesday.

Cursive Writing Skill: Distinguishing uppercase cursive letters with similar forms

CURSIVE WRITING

Unbelievable Uppercase: U/V/W and M/N

Check out some uppercase cursive letters that are easy to confuse. See how **U**, **V**, and **W** are the same. See how **M** and **N** are the same. Think about what your hand does differently when you write them. Practice writing **U**, **V**, **W**, **M**, and **N**. Then write some sentences that use them.

Uppity Veronica Wickers went to Wiggletown Valley University in Vermont.

Mom and Naughty Nicole brought Mister Norbit the Mercury News on Monday.

Cursive Writing Skill: Distinguishing uppercase cursive letters with similar forms

CURSIVE WRITING

Love Those Loops: A/C/O and G/S
Some uppercase cursive letters have loops that look alike. They need extra practice! See how **A**, **C**, and **O** are the same. See how **G** and **S** are the same. Think about what your hand does differently when you write them. Practice writing **A**, **C**, **O**, **G**, and **S**. Then write some sentences that use them.

Aunt Carmen Ortelli told Officer Clyde that Appleton, Colorado, is "Awesome!"

Grandma Shirley met Sylvester Gusto on Sunday in Green Springs, Georgia.

Cursive Writing Skill: Distinguishing uppercase cursive letters with similar forms

CURSIVE WRITING

Cursive! Foiled Again: K/H and J/Y/Z

Drat! These uppercase cursive letters are confusing. See how **K** and **H** are the same. See how **J**, **Y**, and **Z** are the same. Think about what your hand does differently when you write them. Practice writing **K**, **H**, **J**, **Y**, and **Z**. Then write some sentences that use them.

Kanti Haruma and Hoff Kilter sent Kipper Hone's hat to Kittle, New Hampshire.

Yay! You and Jeff Zattle can go to Young's Jazz Fest in Zebraska, New Jersey.

Cursive Writing Skill: Distinguishing uppercase cursive letters with similar forms

CURSIVE WRITING

More Cursive Capitals: Q/L/I and E/X/D

All these loops and curls! 26 cursive letters are just too much! See all the loops in **Q**, **L**, and **I**. See all the curves in **E** and **X**. Think about what your hand does differently when you write them. Practice writing **Q**, **L**, **I**, **E** and **X**. Then write some sentences that use them.

"Quick!" says Queen Leslie of Indiana. "I think Lord Icker is escaping to Lake Quentin!"

Everybody says "Xylophones" when Evan asks for X words. "Enough!" he says.

Cursive Writing Skill: Distinguishing uppercase cursive letters with similar forms

CURSIVE WRITING

A Mailman's Worst Nightmare

Nicole Bakerson is sending a package to Nori Flim. But Nicole's cursive writing is terrible! The mailman will never be able to read it. Can you help by writing Nori's address in cursive on this envelope? Write it as neatly as you can. Nori's address is: Miss Nori T. Flim

          Apartment 4-B

          45 Schoolhouse Lane

          Grundleton, England

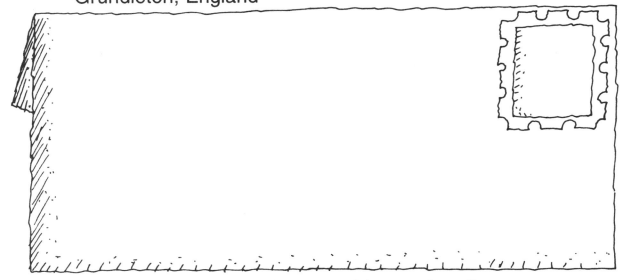

Can you write your name and address on this envelope?

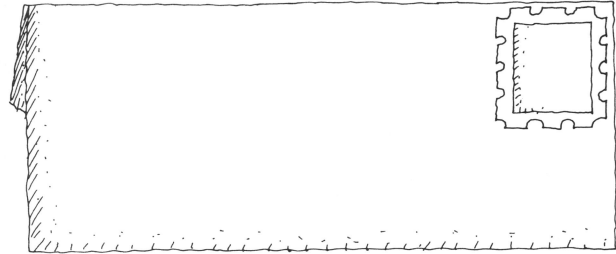

Draw pictures on the stamps! Don't forget to write in how many cents the stamp is worth.

How about this? *Next time someone in your family mails a letter to a friend or relative, ask if you can write the address. Or write a letter of your own to a friend, all in cursive!*

Cursive Writing Skill: Writing cursive letters and words

CURSIVE WRITING

A My Name is Alice

You've probably played this game before. The difference now? Now you can write down your answers in cursive! Think of a name and a place that begin with each letter. Write them in the proper blanks. Remember that names of people and places start with uppercase letters!

my name is…

and I live in…

A

B

C

D

E

F

G

H

I

J

K

L

Cursive Writing Skill: Writing uppercase and lowercase cursive letters

CURSIVE WRITING

my name is...

and I live in...

M

N

O

P

Q

R

S

T

U

V

W

X

Y

Z

Cursive Writing Skill: Writing uppercase and lowercase cursive letters

CURSIVE WRITING

Bad Manners Bart

Bart is always rude. To make matters worse, he always says things twice. Look at the list of his favorite things to say. Then write them in cursive to fill in the blanks below.

YUCK!
YUCK!

Ick ick
Yuck yuck
Achoo achoo
Phew phew
Blech blech
Gag gag

What did Bart say when...

• he saw the lumpy mucky food _____

• he heard Prissy Missy play piano _____

• he saw Claude's painting _____

• he heard Old Mac's joke _____

• he got bored while Jester was talking _____

• Sofia dropped her ice cream cone _____

How about this? *Get a fresh sheet of paper. Think of things that Bart's nice cousin, Bartina, might have said instead. Then write those things in cursive.*

Cursive Writing Skill: Writing uppercase and lowercase cursive letters

CURSIVE WRITING

Cursive Mix-n-Match

Look at the pictures below. Underneath each one is the letter its name starts with. Say the name of the object to yourself. Then write the name in cursive on the blank! You can use lowercase letters to start each word.

Aa _____

Bb _____

Cc _____

Dd _____

Ee _____

Ff _____

Gg _____

Hh _____

Ii _____

Jj _____

Kk _____

Ll _____

Cursive Writing Skill: Writing lowercase cursive letters

CURSIVE WRITING

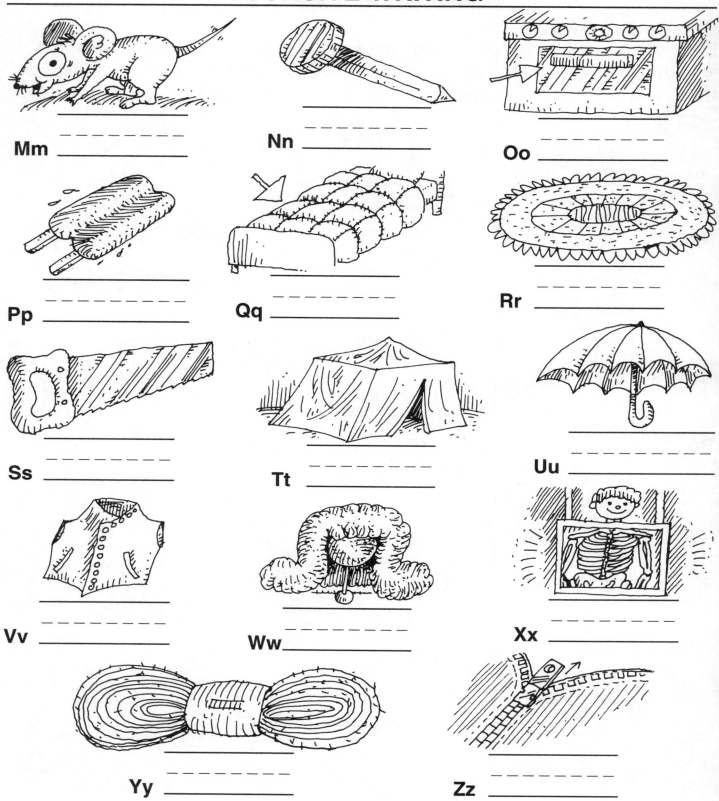

Mm _____

Nn _____

Oo _____

Pp _____

Qq _____

Rr _____

Ss _____

Tt _____

Uu _____

Vv _____

Ww _____

Xx _____

Yy _____

Zz _____

How about this? *Can you make up your own picture-dictionary using words written in cursive? What words would you use for each letter?*

Cursive Writing Skill: Writing lowercase cursive letters

272

CURSIVE WRITING

A Revolting Recipe

Most cooks try to make something delicious. But wouldn't it be fun to make something truly disgusting? Pretend you've found the following ingredients in your kitchen. Write a recipe using them! Use your best cursive handwriting.

Ingredients:
orange juice
soggy lettuce
toothpaste
a carton of milk
stale birthday cake
a stinky onion
pink bubble gum
a chocolate bar
a slice of pizza
chicken soup
a brown banana
a wedge of cheese

Cursive Writing Skill: Writing uppercase and lowercase words

PRACTICE PAGE

PRACTICE PAGE

ANSWERS

Page 8

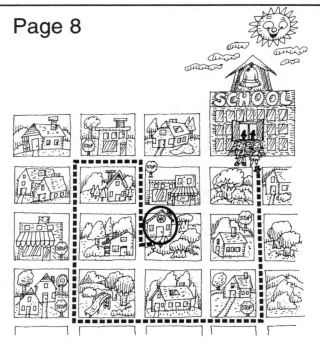

Page 9

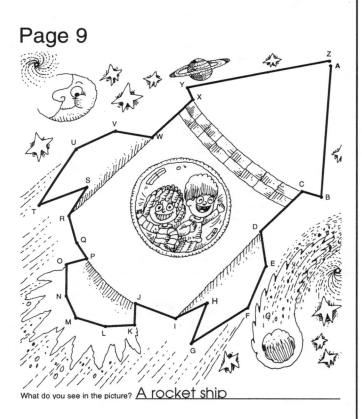

What do you see in the picture? <u>A rocket ship</u>

Page 12

Page 13

Some people are so crabby. I don't know what makes them so **cantankerous**.

I like to **collaborate** with my friends on a project. When we work together, we get a lot done.

I will **ponder** the problem until I find the answer. All I need to do is think very hard about it.

That mouse in the cartoon is so cowardly. I have never seen such a **pusillanimous** mouse.

Page 15

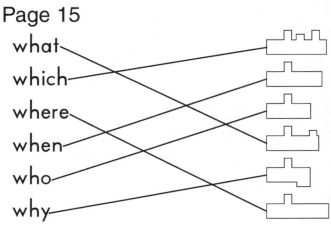

what
which
where
when
who
why

ANSWERS

Page 16

2 The man says, "Waiter, what is that fly doing in my soup?"
3 The waiter says, "The backstroke."
1 A man walks into a restaurant and orders soup.

3 "They are both purple," says the girl. "Except for the chicken."
1 A girl asks a boy, "How is a chicken like a glass of grape juice?"
2 "I don't know," says the boy.

Page 19

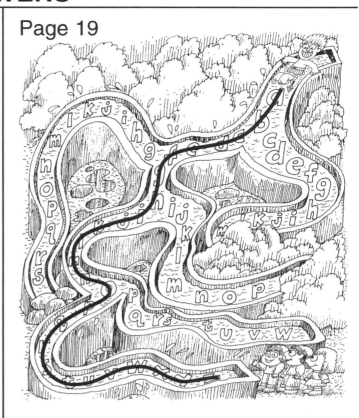

Page 17

1 Doofus is walking backward near the lake.
2 Doofus is trying to climb a tree.
4 Doofus is taking a shortcut through the mud.
3 Doofus is standing on his head in his boat.

Page 20

Put a <u>helmet</u> on your head.
Put kneepads on your <u>knees</u>.
Put <u>gloves</u> on your hands.

| knees | gloves | helmet |

Stay away from <u>people</u> on sidewalks.
Stay away from <u>little</u> kids.
Stay away from all <u>streets</u>.

| streets | people | little |

Go slowly before you go <u>fast</u>.
Watch where you are <u>going</u>.
Stop when you get <u>tired</u>.

| tired | fast | going |

Practice new moves in a <u>safe</u> place.
Wear clothes you can't <u>trip</u> over.
Take good <u>care</u> of your wheels.

| care | safe | trip |

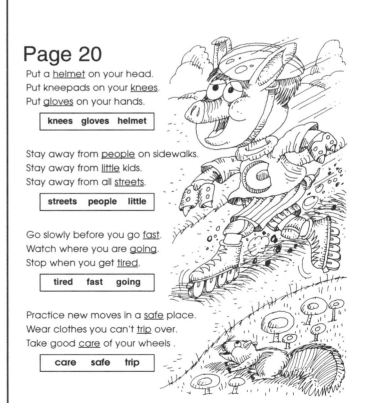

Page 18

Who does something outside? Mom
Who does something inside? Freddy, Dad
Who does something inside and outside? baby
Which one are you most like? Tell why. answers will vary

ANSWERS

Page 21

Things to Wear
shoes
coat
jacket
cap

Things to Eat
pizza
spaghetti
toast
apples

Things to Get Into
answers
will
vary

Things to Stay Out Of
answers
will
vary

Page 22

It happened every day after school. Tony sat down for twenty minutes and worked on his spelling list. He wrote the words. He said them out loud. He had his sister test him. On Friday, Tony took the spelling test in class. Every week it was the same. He always got a perfect score.

How come?
- Tony could spell from the day he was born.
- The teacher made the test really easy.
- (Tony worked hard to learn the words.)

Jessica wanted a new bike more than anything. She saved all of her allowance every other week. She saved all the money from gifts. She did jobs for the lady next door. She was paid a quarter, or a dollar, or sometimes five dollars. It took two years. Then Jessica had her new bike.

How come?
- Jessica begged and begged until her dad bought the bike.
- (Jessica saved almost all of the money she got.)
- The lady next door got the bike for Jessica.

Page 23

Nobody liked the new kid, Tim. No reason—they just didn't like him. Charles was different. He asked Tim to eat a snack with him. He asked about the new kid's old school. Pretty soon Tim began to talk. He was so funny. Then everyone started to like him.

How come?
- Charles made the other kids be nice to the new kid.
- (Everyone saw that Charles liked the new kid.)
- The new kid was a really good singer.

Maisie knew it wasn't fair. Why should her mom have to do all the cooking and cleaning? Why should her mom have to work so hard at home after working so hard at her job? Maisie got her older brother to do some cooking. She got her younger sister to straighten up the house. Maisie spent one hour every day after school doing whatever needed to be done. Soon Maisie's mother wasn't so tired any more.

How come?
- Maisie and her brother started ordering pizza for dinner.
- (Maisie and her brother and sister helped out.)
- Maisie's mother went on a vacation to the Caribbean.

Page 24

Patty and Tim find big hats. They put on tall boots. Each one is carrying a long rope. "Howdy, pardner," Patty calls out to Tim. Tim is singing a song called "Home, Home on the Range." What will Patty and Tim be in the show? How do you know?

Patty and Tim will be a cowboy and cowgirl.

Ashley cuts a whole pile of newspapers into strips. Then she pastes all the strips to a ribbon. She ties the ribbon around her waist. The strips hang from her waist to her knees. Then Ashley makes a necklace of paper flowers. She makes two small ones for her wrists. Then Ashley practices her dance. What kind of dancer will she be? How do you know?

Ashley will be a hula dancer.

ANSWERS

Page 25

Nork from Gork thought the Planet Earth was the most **awesome** place.
To Nork, Earth was (unbelievable and wonderful.)

But Nork thought some things about Earth were **bizarre**.
He said it was (strange) that people moved on things called "feet."

Instead of walking, Nork liked to **levitate**.
Nork (floated in the air) over everyone's head.

Flying among the Earth people made Nork feel **invincible**.
When Nork played tag with the Earth kids, (he would always win.)

One day Nork played tag with a girl who could jump to an amazing (height.)
She finally tagged Nork by jumping to the **altitude** where he was flying!

Page 26

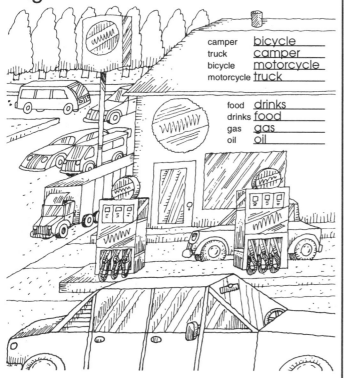

camper	bicycle
truck	camper
bicycle	motorcycle
motorcycle	truck

food	drinks
drinks	food
gas	gas
oil	oil

Page 27

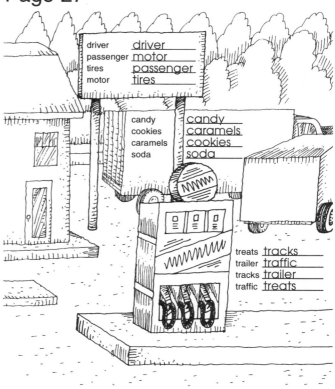

driver	driver
passenger	motor
tires	passenger
motor	tires

candy	candy
cookies	caramels
caramels	cookies
soda	soda

treats	tracks
trailer	traffic
tracks	trailer
traffic	treats

Page 28

_2_ After you find the can and a newspaper, sit down at a table.

_5_ Slide the wrapped can across the table toward your friend. Have him feel the can inside the paper.

_1_ Get an empty soda can and a newspaper.

_4_ When everything is ready, ask your friend to sit across from you at the table.

_3_ Wrap the newspaper tightly around the top and sides of the can.

_9_ Say "Tah-dah!" and wait for the applause!

_10_ If you feel like it, show your friend how you did this disappearing can trick.

_8_ Say "abra-cadabra," "ka-chung ka-chang," or any other magic stuff. Then smash your fist down on the empty newspaper shape.

_6_ Slide the can back toward you, off the edge of the table.

_7_ Let the can fall into your lap, but keep holding the newspaper in the can shape.

ANSWERS

Page 29

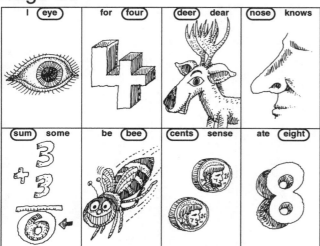

Kelly and <u>I</u> went to the mall.

We <u>ate</u> pizza and drank juice for lunch.

I got a poster with a buzzing <u>bee</u> on it.

The clerk gave me one dollar change from five dollars because the poster cost <u>four</u> dollars.

I also got <u>some</u> stickers and a box of crayons.

Page 30

Some things are strange. Some things are hard to believe. The mystery of the old Hayden house in Maryland is very strange indeed. The house was built in the 1800s and many families lived there through the years. Part of the house is still standing. New parts have been added to make offices and a library.

No one knows when the strange things started happening. Lights began to turn off and on in the office rooms. The electric coffee pot heated up. It wasn't plugged in. A rocking chair would move back and forth. No one was sitting in it. At least there was no one that anyone could see.

People working overtime, late at night, were terrified. They would hear a noise behind them. A door would swing open and closed. Smells of cooking filled the rooms: coffee, soup, bacon and eggs. Workers began to call it "the cooking ghost." But make no mistake, this was no laughing matter.

- Great Fun in Maryland
- (Terror in the Old House)
- Cooking Breakfast
- The Swinging Rocking Chair

Page 31

Believe it or not, some people think there are ghosts everywhere. What are ghosts? They are supposed to be people who died before their time. They might also be people who died in some terrible way. This is odd, because people who say they have seen ghosts also say that the ghosts never seemed angry. They do not mean any harm. Ghosts never hurt people. Okay, some make strange noises. People get scared. But most of the time, ghosts are said to ignore people in a haunted house. Or ghosts may act gently and kindly.

You wouldn't believe some of the things people think about ghosts. Here's one thing. If you were born at night, you will never see a ghost. Here's another thing. Ghosts are supposed to be afraid of other ghosts. If they see themselves in a mirror, they run away. Also, ghosts are supposed to be afraid of water. They will never cross a river or a lake.

Actually, there probably aren't any ghosts. But they are fun to think about!

- Ghosts and Where They Come From
- A Ghost Looks in the Mirror
- Ghostly Walks on Water
- (Facts and Fantasies About Ghosts)

Page 32

The month was November. The year was 1963. The place was a spot in the ocean 70 miles away from Iceland. All week long, the crew of a near-by ship had been smelling a strange chemical odor in the air. Then, on the morning of November 14, it happened! There were shaky rumblings. It was as if there were an earthquake. Smoke and fire appeared to float on top of the water. Then all at once a new island burst up from beneath the sea.

__3__ Fire and smoke appeared to float on the water.
__4__ A new island burst up from the sea.
__1__ People smelled a strange odor in the air.
__2__ The earth shook as if there were an earthquake.

The news spread throughout the world. A new island was born. It was the island they would later call Surtsey. In six days a volcano on the island grew to 230 feet. Explosions of fire and melted rock (called "magma") flew up. Five months later, the island had grown to the size of a half mile. One month later, some of the volcano lava had cooled to form cliffs. Birds came. In June of 1965, the first growing plant was found.

__3__ Cliffs were formed.
__2__ The island was a half mile wide.
__4__ The first plant grew on the island.
__1__ The volcano grew to over 200 feet.

ANSWERS

Page 33

I like to read scary books in the daytime but not at <u>night</u>.

Joke books always make me <u>laugh</u>.

The first book I learned to <u>read</u> had funny pictures.

The hero in a detective story solves a <u>mystery</u>.

Ted is the main <u>character</u> in the book I'm reading.

When I am tired, I like to read a book that is <u>easy</u> to read.

Once I <u>wrote</u> my own book about Halloween.

Sometimes, I take turns reading stories out loud with my <u>friends</u>.

If a book is really good, I read it more than <u>once</u>.

I save my <u>money</u> so I can buy a book or a magazine.

At a secondhand bookstore, I can buy a book for two <u>dollars</u>.

I like a story that has a happy <u>ending</u>.

Page 34

How many wolves might live in one pack?
<u>ten wolves</u>
Why do wolves howl?
<u>They are calling out to each other.</u>
How do wolves play?
<u>They roll around and wrestle.</u>
What do babysitters have to do with wolves?
<u>Old wolves babysit young wolves.</u>
What might a wolf do if it saw a person? What makes you say that?
<u>It might run away, because wolves try to stay away from people.</u>

Page 35

• Meg will go to the mall.
• (Meg will go to school.)
• Meg will go to the movies.

• Jenny will take a nap on the blanket.
• (Jenny and Justin will invite another kid into their fort.)
• Jenny and Justin will invite another kid to go to the movies.

Page 36

gerbil
dog
goldfish
<u>cat</u>

socks
shoes
cap
<u>jacket</u>

pencils
paper
paints
<u>crayons</u>

plate
fork
spoon
<u>cup</u>

carrots
lettuce
cucumbers
<u>beans</u>

juice
milk
soda
<u>water</u>

Page 37

I have a hole in my pants, (so) I will learn to **sew**.

All I **ate** today was (eight) tiny beans.

The **bare** little baby ran outside holding a teddy (bear).

I got (four) apples **for** one dollar.

She (knows) her **nose** hurts when she has a cold.

It doesn't make any **sense** to sell a hot dog for two (cents).

The book I **read** had a (red) cover.

I do **not** have a (knot) in my shoelace.

I will go **to** the show with (two) friends.

I want to **write** your name in the (right) way.

283

ANSWERS

Page 38

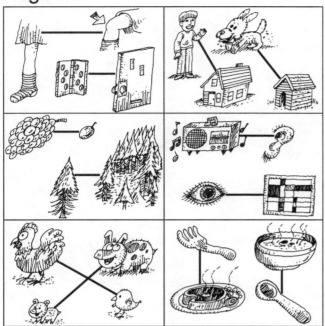

Page 39

Up is to **down** as **in** is to <u>out</u>.

Big is to **bigger** as **tall** is to <u>taller</u>.

Over is to **under** as **top** is to <u>bottom</u>.

Puppy is to **dog** as **kitten** is to <u>cat</u>.

Foot is to **leg** as **hand** is to <u>arm</u>.

Finger is to **hand** as **toe** is to <u>foot</u>.

Hive is to **bee** as **nest** is to <u>bird</u>.

East is to **west** as **north** is to <u>south</u>.

Sight is to **eye** as **hearing** is to <u>ear</u>.

Feathers are to a **chicken** as scales are to a <u>fish</u>.

Page 40

I have some dirt. I have some water and a place out of doors. I'm making it in a sand pail. It feels soft and squishy.

I am making <u>mud</u>.

I don't have any glue for my art work. I do have some flour and water. I put it in a bowl. I mix it with my fingers. I will use this instead of glue.

I am making <u>paste</u>.

I have a camera. I used it to take pictures of my friends. Now I am making a book with drawing paper. I will tie the pages together with yarn. Then I will glue my pictures into the book.

I am making an <u>album</u>.

Page 41

Wendy, Nicole, and Joanna are all names of <u>girls</u>.
Kevin, David, and Anthony are all names of <u>boys</u>.
Red, green, and blue are all <u>colors</u>.
Happy, sad, and excited are words that describe our <u>feelings</u>.
Apples, oranges, and grapes are names of <u>fruits</u>.
Shirt, jeans, and caps are <u>clothing</u>.
Carrots, beans, and peas are <u>vegetables</u>.
Kickball, soccer, and ping-pong are <u>fun</u>.
Books, magazines, and newspapers are things we can <u>read</u>.

ANSWERS

Page 42

__1__ A girl known as Goldilocks entered the Bear residence when no one was home.
__3__ Next she broke a small chair.
__2__ First she went into the kitchen and ate all the porridge.
__4__ When the Bear family came home, they decided not to press charges.

Page 43

__3__ This morning the prince began looking for the girl.
__1__ The prince held a ball last night. He danced with an unknown girl.
__2__ At midnight, the girl ran away from the ball, but dropped her shoe.
__4__ So far, this evening, she has not been found.

"Anyone who knows the name of the prince's dance partner should call right away!" says the newswoman. If you know the answer, write it here:
Cinderella

Page 44

Lauren jumps rope in front of her house. **She** likes to jump rope more than anything.
Who is **She**? Lauren

Kenny sits on the stairs outside his apartment building. **He** is drawing a picture on paper.
Who is **He**? Kenny

You and I are eating ice cream. **We** really are enjoying the sweet, creamy treat.
Who are **We**? You and I

Page 45

Kenny sees a big moving van parked outside his apartment building. **He** thinks **it** is filled with furniture and rugs.
Who is **He**? Kenny
What is **it**? van

Mrs. Grundy likes to put candles in **her** window. Everyone says **they** are pretty.
Who is **her**? Mrs. Grundy
What is **they**? candles

Many of the parents in the neighborhood like to grow flowers in window boxes. Almost every evening, **they** water **them**.
Who is **they**? parents
What is **them**? flowers

Page 46

__3__ Danny and his sister make a necklace of paper clips and hair barrettes.
__4__ Danny's sister tries on the necklace.
__1__ Danny collects paper clips, hair barrettes, and safety pins.
__2__ Danny reminds his sister not to put things in her mouth.
__5__ Danny makes a safety pin bracelet.

Page 47

__3__ Mindy stirs the mixture.
__2__ Kate puts in one cup of salt.
__1__ Mindy puts two cups of flour into the bowl.
__5__ In two hours, the little clay people are hard and dry.
__4__ Mindy and Kate make little clay people.

Page 48

Ben keeps his crayons in a big tin <u>can</u>.
He <u>can</u> spend all day drawing.

Patty likes to <u>rest</u> after she runs a hard race.
Later, she spends the <u>rest</u> of the evening doing quiet things.

Nell wears a <u>band</u> to hold back her hair.
Next year Nell will play in the <u>band</u>.

Stacy breaks the cookie in two pieces that are nearly <u>even</u>.
Stacy doesn't <u>even</u> care if she gets the smaller piece.

Page 49

Toby and Jen sit on the river <u>bank</u> and talk.
Jen tells Toby that she takes her money to a <u>bank</u> to save it.

There are some dogs that don't even <u>bark</u>.
The trunk of a tree has <u>bark</u> on it.

One animal that can be huge, furry, and black is the <u>bear</u>.
They can't <u>bear</u> to look at scary animals in the movies.

People can't understand what you <u>mean</u> if you mumble.
Cassie has no friends because she is so <u>mean</u> to everyone.

Page 51
Answers will vary.

ANSWERS

Page 52

- The Making of Jamestown
- (The True Story of Pocahontas)
- Pocahontas Learns English
- Powhatan's 100 Children

Page 53
Answers will vary.

Page 54

Who lives in the haunted apartment building?

- Ghosts live on 2 floors.
- Skeletons live on 2 floors.
- Monsters live on 1 floor.
- Witches live on 1 floor.

What are the clues?

- 1 family of ghosts lives on the top floor.
- 1 family of skeletons lives directly above the monsters
- 1 family of skeletons lives directly below the monsters.
- The witches live somewhere above all the skeletons and monsters.
- 1 family of ghosts lives below everybody.

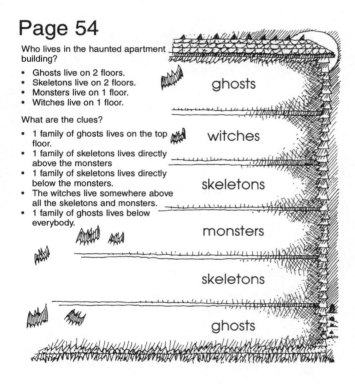

ghosts

witches

skeletons

monsters

skeletons

ghosts

Page 55

Name: Answers will vary

Page 56

Number these sentences **1, 2, 3, 4**:
- 4 — Tinker looked for a shirt and fell in the closet.
- 2 — Tinker stepped out of bed and into a bowl of melted ice cream.
- 1 — Tinker's dog woke him up with loud barking.
- 3 — Tinker made ice cream tracks on the floor.

Number these sentences **5, 6, 7, 8**:
- 8 — Tinker left his room in a mess.
- 5 — Tinker got dressed before he put on his shoes and socks.
- 7 — Tinker put on his shoes over the sticky ice cream socks.
- 6 — Tinker got sticky ice cream inside his socks.

Page 57

Number these sentences **9, 10, 11, 12**:
- 9 — Tinker went into the kitchen.
- 12 — Danny sat down and said, "I smell ice cream feet."
- 10 — Tinker's friend Danny knocked on the kitchen door.
- 11 — Tinker told Danny to come in and have breakfast.

Number these sentences **13, 14, 15, 16**:
- 14 — Tinker's teacher said, "Why do I smell ice cream?"
- 13 — Tinker and Danny walked to school.
- 15 — Tinker ran home after school because dogs were trying to lick his feet.
- 16 — That night Tinker told his mom he is never eating ice cream again.

Page 58

What makes the paper balls go across the table?
Meg and Jo-Jo are blowing them.

What will Meg or Joe-Joe have to do in order to win the race?
Blow harder.

Why do you think this race is harder?
Milk cartons are heavier than paper balls.

Page 59

Write the name of what the picture shows here: sailboat

286

ANSWERS

Page 61

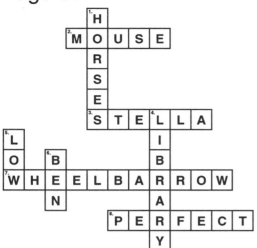

Page 62

$$\begin{array}{cccccccc} 2 & 3 & 4 & 5 & 6 & 7 & 8 & 9 \\ +2 & +3 & +4 & +5 & +6 & +7 & +8 & +9 \\ \hline 4 & 6 & 8 & 10 & 12 & 14 & 16 & 18 \end{array}$$

6 + 6 = 12   6 + 7 = 13   7 + 7 = 14   7 + 8 = 15

8 + 8 = 16   8 + 9 = 17   9 + 9 = 18   9 + 10 = 19

12 − 6 = 6   14 − 7 = 7   16 − 8 = 8   18 − 9 = 9

Page 63

$$\begin{array}{ccccccccc} 16 & 9 & 9 & 2 & 8 & 12 & 14 & 7 & 12 & 5 \\ -8 & +9 & -5 & +2 & -8 & -6 & -7 & +7 & +8 & +6 \\ \hline 8 & 18 & 4 & 4 & 0 & 6 & 7 & 14 & 20 & 11 \end{array}$$

I SEE A GHOUL

$$\begin{array}{cccccccc} 15 & 6 & 10 & 15 & 10 & 7 & 9 & 6 & 4 \\ -7 & +7 & +9 & -8 & -6 & +8 & +5 & +8 & +7 \\ \hline 8 & 13 & 19 & 7 & 4 & 15 & 14 & 14 & 11 \end{array}$$

IN THE POOL

Page 64

(1 + 3) + 4 = 8

1 + (3 + 4) = 8

2 + (3 + 3) = 8

(3 + 4) + 5 = 12

2 + 5 + 3 = 10

7 + 3 + 1 = 11

4 + 0 + 6 = 10

2 + 3 + 6 = 11

Claighorne fell in a hole 7 times in the morning. He fell in the washing machine 3 times in the afternoon. Then he fell in the dog dish 6 times at night. What is the matter with Claighorne, anyway? How many times did he fall all together?

16

ANSWERS

Page 65

7 + 3 = <u>10</u>

4 + <u>7</u> = 11

6 + 3 = <u>9</u>

<u>5</u> + 3 = 8

5 – 2 = <u>3</u>

9 – <u>4</u> = 5

<u>10</u> – 7 = 3

<u>8</u> – 5 = 3

12 – 9 = <u>3</u>

15 – 8 = <u>7</u>

<u>18</u> – 9 = 9

<u>17</u> – 9 = 8

6 ⊕ 1 = 5

9 ⊕ 3 = 12

7 ⊕ 3 = 10

4 ⊕ 9 = 13

13 ⊖ 9 = 4

Page 66

3 + 5 = 8   5 + 3 = 8   8 – 3 = 5   8 – 5 = 3

4 + 5 = <u>9</u>

5 + 4 = <u>9</u>

9 – 5 = <u>4</u>

9 – 4 = <u>5</u>

3 + 2 = <u>5</u>

2 + 3 = <u>5</u>

5 – 2 = <u>3</u>

5 – 3 = <u>2</u>

6 + 4 = <u>10</u>

4 + 6 = <u>10</u>

10 – 4 = <u>6</u>

10 – 6 = <u>4</u>

4 + 3 = <u>7</u>

3 + 4 = <u>7</u>

7 – 3 = <u>4</u>

7 – 4 = <u>3</u>

6 + 9 = <u>15</u>

9 + 6 = <u>15</u>

15 – 6 = <u>9</u>

15 – 9 = <u>6</u>

9 + 8 = <u>17</u>

8 + 9 = <u>17</u>

17 – 9 = <u>8</u>

17 – 8 = <u>9</u>

2 + 8 = 10

8 + 2 = 10

10 – 8 = 2

10 – 2 = 8

Page 67

6 <u>5</u>   13 <u>12</u>   9 <u>8</u>   7 <u>6</u>   1 <u>0</u>

3 <u>5</u>   8 <u>10</u>   5 <u>7</u>   4 <u>6</u>   10 <u>12</u>

2 <u>6</u>   7 <u>16</u>   3 <u>8</u>   8 <u>18</u>   9 <u>20</u>

Page 68

ANSWERS

Page 69

1	2	3	4	5	6	7	8	9	10
11	12	13	14	15	16	17	18	19	20
21	22	23	24	25	26	27	28	29	30
31	32	33	34	35	36	37	38	39	40
41	42	43	44	45	46	47	48	49	50
51	52	53	54	55	56	57	58	59	60
61	62	63	64	65	66	67	68	69	70
71	72	73	74	75	76	77	78	79	80
81	82	83	84	85	86	87	88	89	90
91	92	93	94	95	96	97	98	99	100

- Count by 10s. Use the chart to help you.

  <u>10</u> <u>20</u> <u>30</u> <u>40</u> <u>50</u>

  <u>60</u> <u>70</u> <u>80</u> <u>90</u> <u>100</u>

- Where were all the 10s on the chart?

  <u>In the last column.</u>

- Count by 5s. Write the numbers here.

  <u>5</u> <u>10</u> <u>15</u> <u>20</u> <u>25</u>

  <u>30</u> <u>35</u> <u>40</u> <u>45</u> <u>50</u>

  <u>55</u> <u>60</u> <u>65</u> <u>70</u> <u>75</u>

  <u>80</u> <u>85</u> <u>90</u> <u>95</u> <u>100</u>

- Are all the numbers odd or even when you count by 10? <u>even</u>
- Are all the numbers odd or even when you count by 5? <u>both</u>

Page 70

- Find the ones. How many are there? <u>9</u>
- How many tens are there? <u>2</u>
- How many ones are there in one ten? <u>10</u>
- How many hundreds are there? <u>3</u>
- How many tens in one block of one hundred? <u>10</u>

Write a number for each picture.

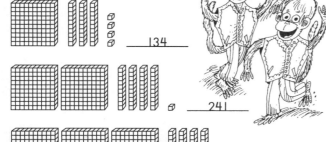

<u>134</u>

<u>241</u>

<u>342</u>

Page 71

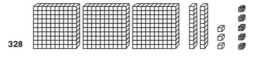

212

312

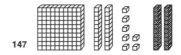

322

163

444

424

Page 72

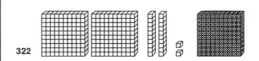

328

147

322

397

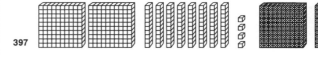

289

ANSWERS

Page 73

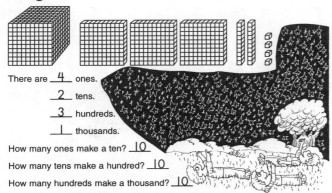

There are __4__ ones.

__2__ tens.

__3__ hundreds.

__1__ thousands.

How many ones make a ten? __10__

How many tens make a hundred? __10__

How many hundreds make a thousand? __10__

Page 74

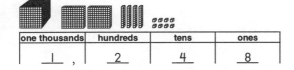

hundreds	tens	ones
2	6	8

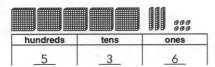

hundreds	tens	ones
5	3	6

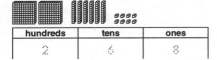

one thousands	hundreds	tens	ones
1 ,	2	4	8

one thousands	hundreds	tens	ones
2 ,	1	6	4

Page 75

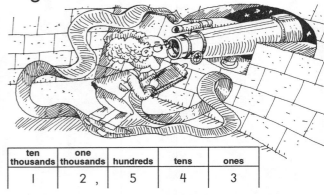

ten thousands	one thousands	hundreds	tens	ones
1	2 ,	5	4	3

We say **twelve thousand, five hundred forty-three.**

How would you write this number? _____12,543_____

hundred thousands	ten thousands	one thousands	hundreds	tens	ones
2	3	4 ,	6	2	9

We say **two hundred thirty-four thousand, six hundred twenty-nine.**

How would you write this number? _____234,629_____

Page 76

twenty-five

2 _5_

three hundred twenty-five

32 _5_

four thousand, three hundred twenty-five

4, _325_

twenty-four thousand, three hundred twenty-five

24, _325_

one hundred twenty-four thousand, three hundred twenty-five

124, _325_

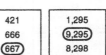

35	421	1,295	10,843	(321,000)
(53)	666	(9,295)	(10,999)	123,000
42	(667)	8,298	9,421	231,000

290

ANSWERS

Page 77

Circle the number that is closer.

58—round up to (60) or down to 50?

23—round up to 30 or down to (20)?

25—round up to (30) or down to 20?

97—round up to (100) or down to 90?

224—round up to 300 or down to (200)?

578—round up to (600) or down to 500?

Page 78

Moe: There were 98 guests at my party. So if I were to round, I'd say there were __100__ guests.

Toe: I was at your party. I think there were exactly 23 guests. So if I were to round, I'd say there were about __20__ guests.

Moe: You are way off. I counted 57 people in my coat closet alone. That is about __60__ people.

Toe: You must be dreaming. I counted 12 people with coats. That is about __10__.

Moe: My guests ate 793 cupcakes at the party. That is about __800__ cupcakes.

Toe: I didn't see cupcakes. But the 172 squishy brown french fries I ate were really good. I couldn't believe I ate about __200__ french fries.

Moe: I can't believe it either. Those were my worms for fishing!

Page 79

32	26	29	36	68	10	55	85
+45	+13	+40	+21	+21	+20	+34	+14
77	39	69	57	89	30	89	99

50	85	20	77	63	89	24	45	27
+49	+12	+30	+11	+33	+10	+44	+42	+72
99	97	50	88	96	99	68	87	99

Page 80

+1	+1	+1
73	35	56
+18	+45	+19
91	80	75

+1	+1	+1	+1
17	24	37	35
+17	+69	+26	+25
34	93	63	60

+1	+1	+1	+1
49	27	34	84
+39	+18	+57	+16
88	45	91	100

Page 81

99	75	34	54
−23	−13	−24	−52
76	62	10	02

87	78	46	39
−66	−27	−10	−28
21	51	36	11

21	53	94	68
−10	−22	−73	−47
11	31	21	21

ANSWERS

Page 82

<pre>
  2 12   3 11   4 17
   3 2   4 1   5 7
 - 1 3   - 3 4   - 2 9
 ─────   ─────   ─────
    19   7   28
</pre>

<pre>
   2 1   4 4   2 6   6 1
 - 1 4   - 2 3   - 1 8   - 5 3
 ─────   ─────   ─────   ─────
     7   21   8   8

   7 8   7 5   9 0   8 4
 - 3 9   - 5 7   - 3 2   - 6 6
 ─────   ─────   ─────   ─────
    39   18   58   18
</pre>

Page 83

<pre>
    12   10   32   30   41   40   57   60
  + 19   + 20   + 38   + 40   + 36   + 40   + 33   + 30
  ────   ────   ────   ────   ────   ────   ────   ────
    31   30   70   70   77   80   90   90

    92   90   39   40   23   20   61   60
  - 54   - 50   - 17   - 20   + 7   - 10   - 24   - 20
  ────   ────   ────   ────   ────   ────   ────   ────
    38   40   22   20   30   30   37   40
</pre>

Page 84

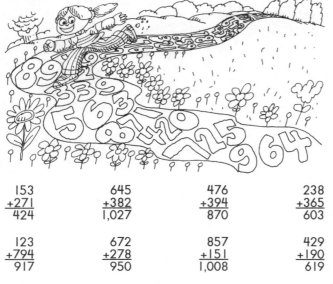

<pre>
    153   645   476   238
  + 271   + 382   + 394   + 365
  ─────   ─────   ─────   ─────
    424   1,027   870   603

    123   672   857   429
  + 794   + 278   + 151   + 190
  ─────   ─────   ─────   ─────
    917   950   1,008   619
</pre>

Page 85

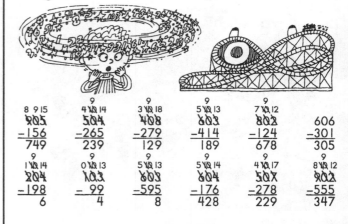

<pre>
  4 12   3 11   5 15   2 17
   5 2 7   4 1 3   6 5 9   8 7 2
 - 1 8 2   - 2 2 2   - 1 8 1   - 1 9 2
 ───────   ───────   ───────   ───────
   3 4 5   1 9 1   4 7 8   1 8 0

  4 12   3 17   6 13   5 11
   5 2 7   4 7 6   7 3 9   6 1 3
 - 3 3 3   - 1 9 2   - 3 4 8   - 2 4 0
 ───────   ───────   ───────   ───────
   1 9 4   2 8 4   3 9 1   3 7 3
</pre>

Page 86

<pre>
  8 9 15   4 10 14   3 10 18   5 10 13   7 10 12
   9 0 5   5 0 4   4 0 8   6 0 3   8 0 2   606
 - 1 5 6   - 2 6 5   - 2 7 9   - 4 1 4   - 1 2 4   - 301
 ───────   ───────   ───────   ───────   ───────   ────
   7 4 9   2 3 9   1 2 9   1 8 9   6 7 8   305

  1 10 14   0 10 13   5 10 13   5 10 14   4 10 17   8 10 12
   2 0 4   1 0 3   6 0 3   6 0 4   5 0 7   9 0 2
 - 1 9 8   -   9 9   - 5 9 5   - 1 7 6   - 2 7 8   - 5 5 5
 ───────   ───────   ───────   ───────   ───────   ───────
       6   4   8   4 2 8   2 2 9   3 4 7
</pre>

Page 87

4 + 4 = 8	5 + 5 = 10	6 + 6 = 12
2 × 4 = 8	2 × 5 = 10	2 × 6 = 12
7 + 7 = 14	8 + 8 = 16	9 + 9 = 18
2 × 7 = 14	2 × 8 = 16	2 × 9 = 18

Mallard has 2 piles of laundry. There are 5 shirts in each pile. Follow the directions below to learn more about Mallard and all of his dirty shirts.

- Write an addition sentence to show how many shirts he has. 5 + 5 = 10
- Write a multiplication sentence to show how many shirts he has. 2 × 5 = 10

ANSWERS

Page 88

9 ×1 — 9	8 ×1 — 8	7 ×1 — 7	6 ×1 — 6	5 ×1 — 5	4 ×1 — 4	3 ×1 — 3	2 ×1 — 2	1 ×1 — 1	0 ×1 — 0
9 ×0 — 0	8 ×0 — 0	7 ×0 — 0	6 ×0 — 0	5 ×0 — 0	4 ×0 — 0	3 ×0 — 0	2 ×0 — 0	1 ×0 — 0	0 ×0 — 0

Page 89

5 + 5 + 5 = _15_	7 + 7 + 7 = _21_	2 + 2 + 2 = _6_
3 × 5 = _15_	3 × 7 = _21_	3 × 2 = _6_
5 × 3 = _15_	7 × 3 = _21_	2 × 3 = _6_
3 × 2 = _6_	3 × 6 = _18_	3 × 9 = _27_
2 × 3 = _6_	6 × 3 = _18_	9 × 3 = _27_
3 × 8 = _24_	3 × 1 = _3_	3 × 0 = _0_
8 × 3 = _24_	1 × 3 = _3_	0 × 3 = _0_

Page 90

	number of groups		number in each group		
	_4_	×	_5_	=	_20_

HERE'S WHAT WE THINK. 4×5=20 So, 5×4=20, Too!

Add or multiply.

2 + 2 + 2 + 2 = _8_   6 + 6 + 6 + 6 = _24_   9 + 9 + 9 + 9 = _36_

4 × 2 = _8_   4 × 6 = _24_   4 × 9 = _36_

2 × 4 = _8_   6 × 4 = _24_   9 × 4 = _36_

2 ×4 — 8	3 ×4 — 12	5 ×4 — 20	0 ×4 — 0	1 ×4 — 4	7 ×4 — 28

Page 91

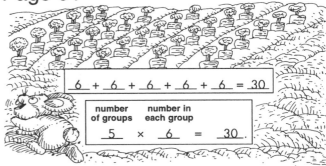

| | _6_ | + | _6_ | + | _6_ | + | _6_ | + | _6_ | = | _30_ |

	number of groups		number in each group		
	_5_	×	_6_	=	_30_

2+2+2+2+2 = _10_   3+3+3+3+3 = _15_   4+4+4+4+4 = _20_

5 × 2 = _10_   5 × 3 = _15_   5 × 4 = _20_

2 × 5 = _10_   3 × 5 = _15_   4 × 5 = _20_

5 × 5 = _25_   5 × 6 = _30_   5 × 1 = _5_

5 × 0 = _0_   5 × 7 = _35_   5 × 8 = _40_

6 ×5 — 30	5 ×6 — 30	8 ×5 — 40	5 ×8 — 40	1 ×5 — 5	5 ×1 — 5	9 ×1 — 9	9 ×2 — 18	9 ×3 — 27	9 ×4 — 36	9 ×5 — 45	9 ×0 — 0

Page 92

	0	1	2	3	4	5	6	7	8	9
0	0	0	0	0	0	0	0	0	0	0
1	0	1	2	3	4	5	6	7	8	9
2	0	2	4	6	8	10	12	14	16	18
3	0	3	6	9	12	15	18	21	24	27
4	0	4	8	12	16	20	24	28	32	36
5	0	5	10	15	20	25	30	35	40	45
6	0	6	12	18	24	30	36	42	48	54
7	0	7	14	21	28	35	42	49	56	63
8	0	8	16	24	32	40	48	56	64	72
9	0	9	18	27	36	45	54	63	72	81

7 ×7 — 49	4 ×9 — 36	8 ×3 — 24	7 ×8 — 56	8 ×9 — 72	5 ×0 — 0

ANSWERS

Page 93

$$\begin{array}{r}3\\\times6\\\hline18\end{array}\qquad\begin{array}{r}8\\\times2\\\hline16\end{array}\qquad\begin{array}{r}8\\\times6\\\hline48\end{array}\qquad\begin{array}{r}2\\\times7\\\hline14\end{array}\qquad\begin{array}{r}7\\\times0\\\hline0\end{array}$$

$$\begin{array}{r}6\\\times4\\\hline24\end{array}\qquad\begin{array}{r}8\\\times7\\\hline56\end{array}\qquad\begin{array}{r}7\\\times6\\\hline42\end{array}\qquad\begin{array}{r}6\\\times7\\\hline42\end{array}\qquad\begin{array}{r}8\\\times5\\\hline40\end{array}$$

$$\begin{array}{r}6\\\times1\\\hline6\end{array}\qquad\begin{array}{r}4\\\times8\\\hline32\end{array}\qquad\begin{array}{r}8\\\times9\\\hline72\end{array}\qquad\begin{array}{r}9\\\times7\\\hline63\end{array}\qquad\begin{array}{r}8\\\times8\\\hline64\end{array}$$

$$\begin{array}{r}1\\\times8\\\hline8\end{array}\qquad\begin{array}{r}5\\\times6\\\hline30\end{array}\qquad\begin{array}{r}7\\\times3\\\hline\cancel{2}\,21\end{array}$$

$$\begin{array}{r}3\\\times8\\\hline24\end{array}\qquad\begin{array}{r}4\\\times7\\\hline\cancel{2}\,28\end{array}\qquad\begin{array}{r}0\\\times6\\\hline\cancel{0}\,0\end{array}$$

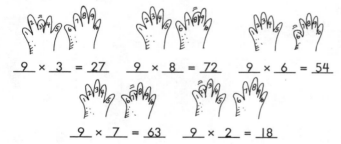

Page 94

$9 \times 3 = 27$ $9 \times 8 = 72$ $9 \times 6 = 54$

$9 \times 7 = 63$ $9 \times 2 = 18$

Page 95

$4 \times 3 = 12$ $4 \times 4 = 16$
$12 \div 4 = 3$ $16 \div 4 = 4$

$4 \times 5 = 20$	$4 \times 7 = 28$	$4 \times 9 = 36$	$4 \times 6 = 24$
$20 \div 4 = 5$	$28 \div 4 = 7$	$36 \div 9 = 4$	$24 \div 4 = 6$
$2 \times 3 = 6$	$2 \times 9 = 18$	$2 \times 7 = 14$	$2 \times 8 = 16$
$6 \div 2 = 3$	$18 \div 2 = 9$	$14 \div 2 = 7$	$16 \div 2 = 8$

Page 96

$2 \times 4 = 8$	$3 \times 6 = 18$	$4 \times 8 = 32$	$4 \times 9 = 36$	$3 \times 5 = 15$
$4 \times 2 = 8$	$6 \times 3 = 18$	$8 \times 4 = 32$	$9 \times 4 = 36$	$5 \times 3 = 15$
$8 \div 2 = 4$	$18 \div 3 = 6$	$32 \div 4 = 8$	$36 \div 4 = 9$	$15 \div 3 = 5$
$8 \div 4 = 2$	$18 \div 6 = 3$	$32 \div 8 = 4$	$36 \div 9 = 4$	$15 \div 5 = 3$

Page 97

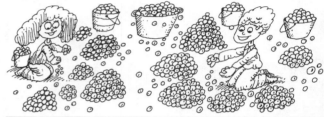

$5 \times 6 = 30$	$7 \times 4 = 28$	$3 \times 8 = 24$	$9 \times 2 = 18$
$6 \times 5 = 30$	$4 \times 7 = 28$	$8 \times 3 = 24$	$2 \times 9 = 18$
$30 \div 6 = 5$	$28 \div 4 = 7$	$24 \div 8 = 3$	$18 \div 2 = 9$
$30 \div 5 = 6$	$28 \div 7 = 4$	$24 \div 3 = 8$	$18 \div 9 = 2$
$6 \times 9 = 54$	$7 \times 8 = 56$	$9 \times 7 = 63$	$6 \times 7 = 42$
$9 \times 6 = 54$	$8 \times 7 = 56$	$7 \times 9 = 63$	$7 \times 6 = 42$
$54 \div 9 = 6$	$56 \div 8 = 7$	$63 \div 7 = 9$	$42 \div 7 = 6$
$54 \div 6 = 9$	$56 \div 7 = 8$	$63 \div 9 = 7$	$42 \div 6 = 7$

Page 98

$6 \times 8 = 48$	$2 \div 2 = 1$	$3 + 2 = 5$	$2 - 2 = 0$
$2 \times 3 = 6$	$3 + 1 = 4$	$6 \div 2 = 3$	$4 \times 5 = 20$
$12 \div 3 = 4$	$7 \times 2 = 14$	$5 + 7 = 12$	$18 - 6 = 12$
$8 \div 2 = 10$	$8 - 2 = 6$	$8 \times 2 = 16$	$8 \div 2 = 4$
$20 - 6 = 14$	$20 + 3 = 23$	$20 \div 2 = 10$	$20 + 10 = 30$

ANSWERS

Page 99

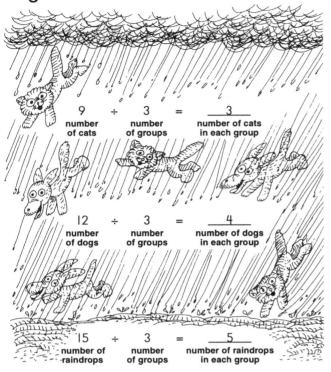

9 ÷ 3 = 3
number of cats | number of groups | number of cats in each group

12 ÷ 3 = 4
number of dogs | number of groups | number of dogs in each group

15 ÷ 3 = 5
number of raindrops | number of groups | number of raindrops in each group

Page 100

÷	0	2	4	6	8	10	12	14	16	18	20
2	0	1	2	3	4	5	6	7	8	9	10
	T	W	E	B	A	S	H	O	M	I	R

÷	0	6	12	18	24	30	36	42	48	54	60
6	0	1	2	3	4	5	6	7	8	9	10
	T	W	E	B	A	S	H	O	M	I	R

W H E R E I S T H E
1 6 2 10 2 9 5 0 6 2

B A T H R O O M?
3 4 0 6 10 7 7 8

Page 101

7 ★ ×9	2 ×8	4 ★ ×4	3 ×8
54	(16)	18	(22)
(63)	28	8	(24)
56	(14)	(16)	38

5 ×6	7 ★ ×3	2 ×6	7 ×4
25	20	(12)	(21)
(30)	(21)	26	(28)
(35)	22	(10)	27

★36 ÷ 9 =	5	(4)	3
25 ÷ 5 =	(5)	4	(6)
18 ÷ 2 =	(6)	3	(9)
★20 ÷ 4 =	4	6	(5)
42 ÷ 7 =	7	(8)	(6)
★54 ÷ 6 =	(9)	8	6
32 ÷ 4 =	(8)	6	(9)
★45 ÷ 5 =	(9)	4	8
★72 ÷ 9 =	7	(8)	2

Page 102

6 (>) 2
2 (<) 6
57 (<) 91
91 (>) 57
100 (>) 10
45 (<) 50
17 (>) 13
3 (>) 0
343 (<) 444
175 (>) 172
848 (>) 745
1,000 (<) 1,222

ANSWERS

Page 103

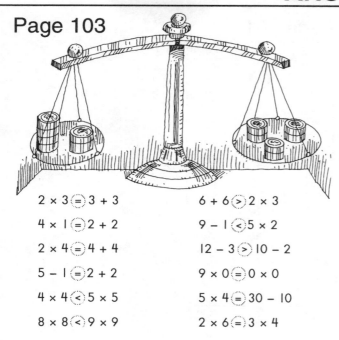

$2 \times 3 \;(=)\; 3 + 3$ $6 + 6 \;(>)\; 2 \times 3$

$4 \times 1 \;(=)\; 2 + 2$ $9 - 1 \;(<)\; 5 \times 2$

$2 \times 4 \;(=)\; 4 + 4$ $12 - 3 \;(>)\; 10 - 2$

$5 - 1 \;(=)\; 2 + 2$ $9 \times 0 \;(=)\; 0 \times 0$

$4 \times 4 \;(<)\; 5 \times 5$ $5 \times 4 \;(=)\; 30 - 10$

$8 \times 8 \;(<)\; 9 \times 9$ $2 \times 6 \;(=)\; 3 \times 4$

Page 104

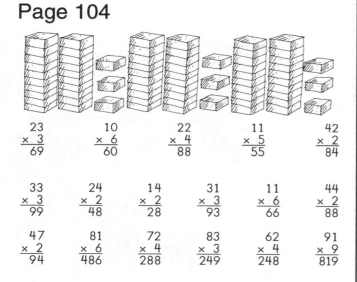

$$\begin{array}{r} 23 \\ \times\,3 \\ \hline 69 \end{array} \qquad \begin{array}{r} 10 \\ \times\,6 \\ \hline 60 \end{array} \qquad \begin{array}{r} 22 \\ \times\,4 \\ \hline 88 \end{array} \qquad \begin{array}{r} 11 \\ \times\,5 \\ \hline 55 \end{array} \qquad \begin{array}{r} 42 \\ \times\,2 \\ \hline 84 \end{array}$$

$$\begin{array}{r} 33 \\ \times\,3 \\ \hline 99 \end{array} \quad \begin{array}{r} 24 \\ \times\,2 \\ \hline 48 \end{array} \quad \begin{array}{r} 14 \\ \times\,2 \\ \hline 28 \end{array} \quad \begin{array}{r} 31 \\ \times\,3 \\ \hline 93 \end{array} \quad \begin{array}{r} 11 \\ \times\,6 \\ \hline 66 \end{array} \quad \begin{array}{r} 44 \\ \times\,2 \\ \hline 88 \end{array}$$

$$\begin{array}{r} 47 \\ \times\,2 \\ \hline 94 \end{array} \quad \begin{array}{r} 81 \\ \times\,6 \\ \hline 486 \end{array} \quad \begin{array}{r} 72 \\ \times\,4 \\ \hline 288 \end{array} \quad \begin{array}{r} 83 \\ \times\,3 \\ \hline 249 \end{array} \quad \begin{array}{r} 62 \\ \times\,4 \\ \hline 248 \end{array} \quad \begin{array}{r} 91 \\ \times\,9 \\ \hline 819 \end{array}$$

Page 105

$$3\overline{)39}^{\,13} \qquad 2\overline{)18}^{\,9} \qquad 2\overline{)68}^{\,34} \qquad 2\overline{)42}^{\,21}$$

$$4\overline{)88}^{\,22} \qquad 6\overline{)66}^{\,11} \qquad 7\overline{)70}^{\,10} \qquad 3\overline{)96}^{\,32}$$

Page 106

$$\begin{array}{r} {\scriptstyle +2} \\ 14 \\ \times\,6 \\ \hline 64 \\ \hline 84 \end{array} \quad \begin{array}{r} {\scriptstyle +1} \\ 17 \\ \times\,2 \\ \hline 24 \\ \hline 34 \end{array} \quad \begin{array}{r} {\scriptstyle +3} \\ 17 \\ \times\,5 \\ \hline 55 \\ \hline 85 \end{array} \quad \begin{array}{r} {\scriptstyle +1} \\ 26 \\ \times\,3 \\ \hline 68 \\ \hline 78 \end{array} \quad \begin{array}{r} {\scriptstyle +1} \\ 13 \\ \times\,5 \\ \hline 55 \\ \hline 65 \end{array}$$

$$\begin{array}{r} {\scriptstyle +1} \\ 16 \\ \times\,3 \\ \hline 48 \end{array} \quad \begin{array}{r} {\scriptstyle +2} \\ 27 \\ \times\,3 \\ \hline 81 \end{array} \quad \begin{array}{r} {\scriptstyle +4} \\ 19 \\ \times\,5 \\ \hline 95 \end{array} \quad \begin{array}{r} {\scriptstyle +1} \\ 38 \\ \times\,2 \\ \hline 76 \end{array} \quad \begin{array}{r} {\scriptstyle +2} \\ 14 \\ \times\,7 \\ \hline 98 \end{array}$$

$$\begin{array}{r} {\scriptstyle +2} \\ 13 \\ \times\,7 \\ \hline 91 \end{array} \quad \begin{array}{r} {\scriptstyle +3} \\ 16 \\ \times\,6 \\ \hline 96 \end{array} \quad \begin{array}{r} {\scriptstyle +1} \\ 23 \\ \times\,4 \\ \hline 92 \end{array} \quad \begin{array}{r} {\scriptstyle +1} \\ 49 \\ \times\,2 \\ \hline 98 \end{array} \quad \begin{array}{r} {\scriptstyle +2} \\ 17 \\ \times\,4 \\ \hline 68 \end{array}$$

Page 107

$$\begin{array}{r} {\scriptstyle +4} \\ 39 \\ \times\,5 \\ \hline 195 \end{array} \qquad \begin{array}{r} {\scriptstyle +2} \\ 54 \\ \times\,6 \\ \hline 324 \end{array} \qquad \begin{array}{r} {\scriptstyle +3} \\ 39 \\ \times\,4 \\ \hline 156 \end{array} \qquad \begin{array}{r} {\scriptstyle +2} \\ 24 \\ \times\,6 \\ \hline 144 \end{array} \qquad \begin{array}{r} {\scriptstyle +1} \\ 32 \\ \times\,9 \\ \hline 288 \end{array}$$

$$\begin{array}{r} {\scriptstyle +2} \\ 36 \\ \times\,4 \\ \hline 144 \end{array}$$

$$\begin{array}{r} {\scriptstyle +1} \\ 76 \\ \times\,2 \\ \hline 152 \end{array}$$

ANSWERS

Page 108

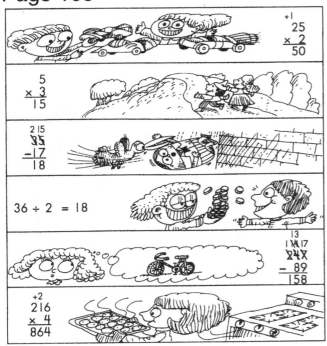

$$\begin{array}{r} +1 \\ 25 \\ \times\ 2 \\ \hline 50 \end{array}$$

$$\begin{array}{r} 5 \\ \times\ 3 \\ \hline 15 \end{array}$$

$$\begin{array}{r} 2\ 15 \\ \cancel{35} \\ -17 \\ \hline 18 \end{array}$$

$$36 \div 2 = 18$$

$$\begin{array}{r} 13 \\ 1\ \cancel{M}\ 17 \\ \cancel{24}\cancel{7} \\ -\ 89 \\ \hline 158 \end{array}$$

$$\begin{array}{r} +2 \\ 216 \\ \times\ 4 \\ \hline 864 \end{array}$$

Page 109

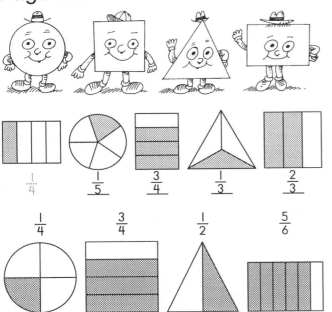

$\dfrac{1}{5}$ $\dfrac{3}{4}$ $\dfrac{1}{3}$ $\dfrac{2}{3}$

$\dfrac{1}{4}$ $\dfrac{3}{4}$ $\dfrac{1}{2}$ $\dfrac{5}{6}$

Page 110

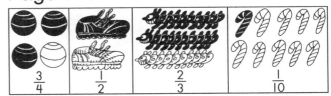

$\dfrac{3}{4}$ $\dfrac{1}{2}$ $\dfrac{2}{3}$ $\dfrac{1}{10}$

$\dfrac{5}{10}$

Page 111

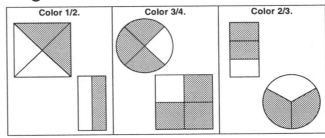

Color 1/2.   Color 3/4.   Color 2/3.

Page 112

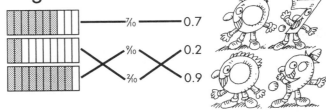

$\dfrac{7}{10}$ —— 0.7

$\dfrac{9}{10}$ ⨯ 0.2

$\dfrac{2}{10}$ ⨯ 0.9

forty-six and eight tenths

tens	ones	tenths
4	6 .	8

46.8

twelve and three tenths

tens	ones	tenths
1	2 .	3

12.3

seventy-nine and one tenth

tens	ones	tenths
7	9 .	1

79.1

sixty-two and four tenths

tens	ones	tenths
6	2 .	4

62.4

297

ANSWERS

Page 113

$\frac{5}{10}$ ___0.5___   0.2 ___$\frac{2}{10}$___

$\frac{3}{10}$ ___0.3___   0.9 ___$\frac{9}{10}$___

$\frac{4}{10}$ ___0.4___   0.3 ___$\frac{3}{10}$___

$\frac{8}{10}$ ___0.8___   0.7 ___$\frac{7}{10}$___

$1 \frac{6}{10} = 1.6$

$3 \frac{2}{10} = 3.2$

$2 \frac{8}{10} = 2.8$

Page 114

```
  4.7      5.2      7.1      6.8
 +2.2     +0.6     +4.2    +10.1
 ----     ----     ----    -----
  6.9      5.8     11.3     16.9
```

```
  5.2      7.3      2.7     13.5     43.6
 +2.5     +7.9     +3.8    + 4.7    +22.6
 ----     ----     ----    -----    -----
  7.7     15.2      6.5     18.2     66.2
```

```
 72.8    100.8     98.6    125.25    460.6
+79.5   + 19.4    +98.6   +180.90   +352.9
-----   ------    -----   -------   ------
152.3    120.2    197.2    306.15    813.5
```

Page 115

```
  4.9      6.6      5.8      2.7      6.2
 -2.7     -4.3     -1.8     -0.6     -6.1
 ----     ----     ----     ----     ----
  2.2      2.3      4.0      2.1      0.1
```

```
 7 17     5 13     2 18     0 12     4 15
 8.7      6.3      3.8      1.2      5.5
-3.9     -1.8     -2.9     -0.4     -4.8
----     ----     ----     ----     ----
 4.8      4.5      0.9      0.8      0.7
```

```
 8 15    1 11 17   0 10 16  0 18 7 11  2 12 3 15
79.5     22.7      10.6     188.1      324.5
-72.8    - 6.8     - 3.9    - 94.4     -131.8
-----    -----     ----     -----      ------
  6.7     15.9      6.7      93.7       192.7
```

Page 117

```
     9
  4 10 10
  $5.00
  -1.29
  -----
  $3.71
```

```
     9
  2 10 10
  $3.00
  -1.55
  -----
  $1.45
```

```
  6 10
  $7.00
  -4.50
  -----
  $2.50
```

```
     9
  8 10 10
  $9.00
  -8.95
  -----
  $0.05
```

```
  $3.99
  -2.75
  -----
  $1.24
```

```
  4 16
  $5.65
  -1.82
  -----
  $3.83
```

```
  1 13
  $2.34
  - .50
  -----
  $1.84
```

```
  5 12
  $6.25
  -5.45
  -----
  $0.80
```

Page 118

Lerd: 75¢
Gerd: 56¢
Savings: ___19¢___

Lerd: 98¢
Gerd: 50¢
Savings: ___48¢___

Lerd: 42¢
Gerd: 17¢
Savings: ___25¢___

Lerd: $1.19
Gerd: 89¢
Savings: ___30¢___

Lerd: $2.50
Gerd: $1.39
Savings: ___$1.11___

Lerd: $3.14
Gerd: $2.89
Savings: ___25¢___

ANSWERS

Page 120

| 9
2 10 0
$300.00
−142.00
$158.00 | 9
3 10 0
$400.00
−168.00
$232.00 | 9
7 10 0
$800.00
−267.00
$533.00 | $625.00
−214.00
$411.00 | 8 17
$976.00
−782.00
$194.00 |

| 6 13 12
$742.00
−357.00
$385.00 | 9 9 9
2 10 10 10 10
$300.00
−163.25
$136.75 | 0 17
$551.75
−340.80
$210.95 | 1 13 13 515
$243.65
−175.28
$ 68.37 |

Page 121

Pam	$31.00
(Bam)	$24.00
	$7.00

Dick	$15.05
(Doc)	12.95
	$2.10

Mollie	$110.95
(Paulie)	$98.20
	$12.75

Sam	$204.57
(Tam)	$178.43
	$26.14

Page 122

Write a time for each clock.   Draw hands to show the time.

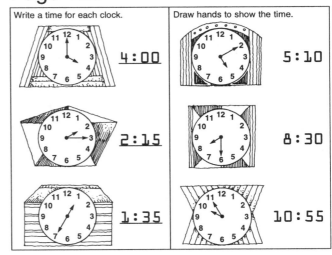

4:00   5:10

2:15   8:30

1:35   10:55

Page 123

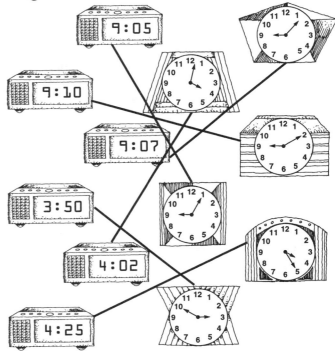

9:05

9:10

9:07

3:50

4:02

4:25

299

ANSWERS

Page 124

Gerald got on the bus.

Gerald arrived at the mall.

Gerald and Ginger arrived at Ginger's house.

Gerald got into Ginger's mom's car.

How many minutes did Gerald spend on the bus? __30__

How many minutes did it take Gerald to find Ginger? __25__

How long was Gerald's car ride home? __35__

Page 126

your finger	inch
your hand	inch
your foot	inch
your height	foot
the height of a parent	foot
the length of a long table	yard
one sticker	inch
a crayon box	inch
length of cloth for a ghost costume	foot
the width of a room	yard

Page 127

____ Two people with a half-gallon of juice can each drink 2 quarts.

____ I drank 8 cups of juice over the weekend, so I drank 2 quarts.

__X__ I spilled 8 half-gallons of milk on the floor. That means I'm standing in a 3-gallon puddle!

4-gallon puddle

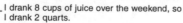

Page 128

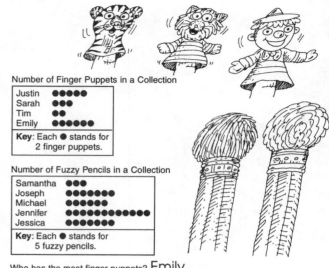

Number of Finger Puppets in a Collection

Justin	●●●●●
Sarah	●●●
Tim	●●
Emily	●●●●●●

Key: Each ● stands for 2 finger puppets.

Number of Fuzzy Pencils in a Collection

Samantha	●●●
Joseph	●●●●●●●
Michael	●●●●●●●●
Jennifer	●●●●●●●●●●●●
Jessica	●●●●●●●●

Key: Each ● stands for 5 fuzzy pencils.

Who has the most finger puppets? __Emily__

How many does that person have? __12__

Who has the smallest amount of fuzzy pencils? __Samantha__

Who has the greatest amount of fuzzy pencils? __Jennifer__

How many more does that person have? __45__

Page 129

	1	2	3	4	5	6	7	8	9	10
Week 1	▓	▓	▓							
Week 2	▓	▓	▓	▓	▓	▓				
Week 3	▓	▓	▓	▓						
Week 4	▓	▓	▓	▓	▓	▓	▓			
Week 5	▓	▓	▓	▓	▓	▓	▓	▓	▓	▓
Week 6	▓	▓								
Week 7	▓	▓	▓	▓	▓	▓	▓	▓	▓	
Week 8	▓	▓	▓	▓	▓	▓	▓	▓	▓	▓
Week 9	▓	▓	▓	▓	▓	▓	▓	▓		
Week 10	▓	▓	▓	▓	▓	▓	▓	▓	▓	▓

How many words did Jody get right in week 1? __3__

How many words did Jody get right in week 2? __6__

Now fill in the bars for the other weeks.

- **Week 3:** Jody has 4 correct spelling words.
- **Week 4:** Jody has 7 correct spelling words.
- **Week 5:** Jody has 10 correct spelling words.
- **Week 6:** Jody has 2 correct spelling words.
- **Week 7:** Jody has 9 correct spelling words.
- **Week 8:** Jody has 10 correct spelling words.
- **Week 9:** Jody has 8 correct spelling words.
- **Week 10:** Jody has 10 correct spelling words.

During which week did Jody get the lowest score? __Week 6__

During which weeks did Jody get a perfect score? __5, 8, 10__

ANSWERS

Page 131

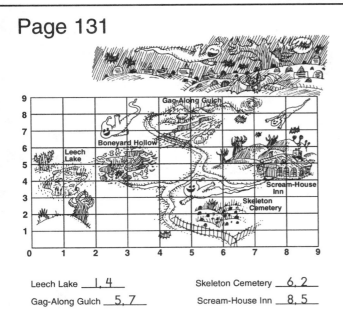

Leech Lake __1, 4__

Gag-Along Gulch __5, 7__

Skeleton Cemetery __6, 2__

Scream-House Inn __8, 5__

Page 166

Person	Place	Thing
girl	store	balloon
boy	Fitting Room	sign
clerk	Upstairs	backpack

Page 167

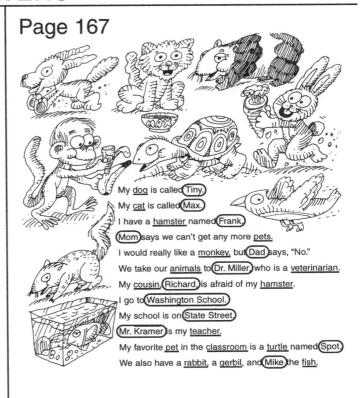

My <u>dog</u> is called (Tiny.)

My <u>cat</u> is called (Max.)

I have a <u>hamster</u> named (Frank.)

(Mom) says we can't get any more <u>pets</u>.

I would really like a <u>monkey</u>, but (Dad) says, "No."

We take our <u>animals</u> to (Dr. Miller,) who is a <u>veterinarian</u>.

My <u>cousin</u>, (Richard,) is afraid of my <u>hamster</u>.

I go to (Washington School.)

My school is on (State Street.)

(Mr. Kramer) is my <u>teacher</u>.

My favorite <u>pet</u> in the <u>classroom</u> is a <u>turtle</u> named (Spot.)

We also have a <u>rabbit</u>, a <u>gerbil</u>, and (Mike) the <u>fish</u>.

Page 169

Sometimes (I) watch <u>television</u> alone.

Sometimes (I) play <u>games</u> alone.

(I) play <u>video games</u>.

(I) like to make <u>faces</u> in the <u>mirror</u>.

(I) play <u>games</u> with my <u>family</u>, too.

(We) also read <u>books</u> together.

Sometimes, <u>Dad</u> reads to (us.)

Sometimes, <u>Dad</u> reads to just (me) all alone.

(I) like when <u>Dad</u> reads funny <u>stories</u>.

Sometimes, a <u>friend</u> reads with (me.)

Sometimes, (we) ask <u>Mom</u> to read a <u>book</u>.

<u>Mom</u> likes reading to (us.)

ANSWERS

Page 170

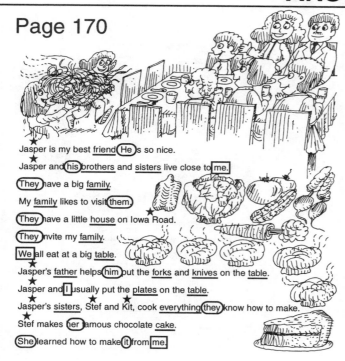

Jasper is my best <u>friend</u> (He) is so nice.

Jasper and (his) <u>brothers</u> and <u>sisters</u> live close to <u>me.</u>

(They) have a big <u>family.</u>

My <u>family</u> likes to visit (them.)

(They) have a little <u>house</u> on Iowa Road.

(They) invite my <u>family.</u>

(We) all eat at a big <u>table.</u>

Jasper's <u>father</u> helps (him) put the <u>forks</u> and <u>knives</u> on the <u>table.</u>

Jasper and (I) usually put the <u>plates</u> on the <u>table.</u>

Jasper's <u>sisters</u>, Stef and Kit, cook <u>everything</u> (they) know how to make.

Stef makes (her) famous chocolate <u>cake.</u>

(She) learned how to make (it) from (me.)

Page 171

Write a pronoun you might use instead of the noun.

Your name ___me___

Mr. Gremlin ___he___

Mrs. North ___she___

A policeman ___he___

A wild wolf ___it___

Lisa, Josh, Tony ___they___

A mystery note ___it___

A boarded-up house ___it___

A bowl of poisonous vapor ___it___

Your next-door neighbor's girl poodle, Puffette ___she___

Page 172

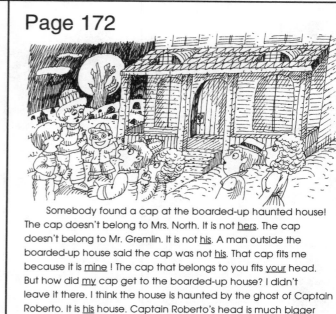

Somebody found a cap at the boarded-up haunted house! The cap doesn't belong to Mrs. North. It is not <u>hers</u>. The cap doesn't belong to Mr. Gremlin. It is not <u>his</u>. A man outside the boarded-up house said the cap was not <u>his</u>. That cap fits me because it is <u>mine</u> ! The cap that belongs to you fits <u>your</u> head. But how did <u>my</u> cap get to the boarded-up house? I didn't leave it there. I think the house is haunted by the ghost of Captain Roberto. It is <u>his</u> house. Captain Roberto's head is much bigger than <u>mine</u>. I don't know why he wanted my small hat. <u>His</u> hat fits him perfectly.

Page 173

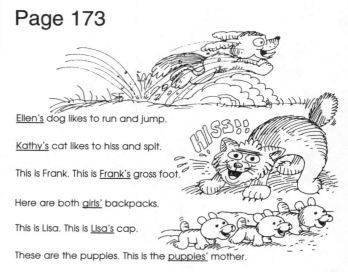

<u>Ellen's</u> dog likes to run and jump.

<u>Kathy's</u> cat likes to hiss and spit.

This is Frank. This is <u>Frank's</u> gross foot.

Here are both <u>girls'</u> backpacks.

This is Lisa. This is <u>Lisa's</u> cap.

These are the puppies. This is the <u>puppies'</u> mother.

ANSWERS

Page 174

crayon <u>crayons</u>
book <u>books</u>
box <u>boxes</u>
paper <u>papers</u>
pencil <u>pencils</u>
fork <u>forks</u>
glass <u>glasses</u>
lunch <u>lunches</u>
bunch <u>bunches</u>
pizza <u>pizzas</u>
lady <u>ladies</u>
penny <u>pennies</u>
baby <u>babies</u>
shirt <u>shirts</u>
fox <u>foxes</u>
bush <u>bushes</u>
bird <u>birds</u>
mouse <u>mice</u>

Page 175

Jake <u>walks</u>.
Sam <u>runs</u> everywhere he goes.
Hettie <u>dances</u> to the music on the radio.
Calvin <u>spins</u> around and around the room.
Anthony <u>claps</u> his hands.
Ashley <u>draws</u> a picture.
Nicole <u>snaps</u> her fingers.
The dog <u>wags</u> its tail.
The cat <u>purrs</u>.
The wind <u>blows</u> around the house.
The snow <u>falls</u> in a thick white blanket.
The grandfather clock <u>strikes</u> 9:00.

Page 177

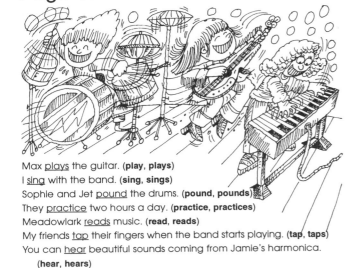

Max <u>plays</u> the guitar. (**play, plays**)
I <u>sing</u> with the band. (**sing, sings**)
Sophie and Jet <u>pound</u> the drums. (**pound, pounds**)
They <u>practice</u> two hours a day. (**practice, practices**)
Meadowlark <u>reads</u> music. (**read, reads**)
My friends <u>tap</u> their fingers when the band starts playing. (**tap, taps**)
You can <u>hear</u> beautiful sounds coming from Jamie's harmonica.
   (**hear, hears**)
He <u>bends</u> down close to the floor when he plays. (**bend, bends**)
People <u>clap</u> when he is finished playing. (**clap, claps**)
Ringo <u>claps</u> too because Jamie is so good. (**clap, claps**)
We all <u>listen</u> to our favorite groups on CDs. (**listen, listens**)

Page 178

Underline a verb in each sentence.
I <u>walk</u> to school.
I <u>walked</u> yesterday.
My dog <u>barks</u> as I leave for school.
My dog <u>barked</u> really loudly this morning.
My mom and dad <u>wave</u> to me when I leave.
Yesterday, I <u>waved</u> back at them.
When we were in kindergarten, we <u>played</u> a lot in school.
Now we <u>play</u> only at special times.
I <u>add</u> lots of numbers and check the answer on my calculator.
Only last week, I <u>added</u> a column of ten numbers.
After school, I <u>painted</u> a mural showing my neighborhood.
I <u>paint</u> the sun to finish my picture.
Write the verbs you underlined in the correct column below.

Present tense verbs	Past tense verbs
<u>walk</u>	<u>walked</u>
<u>barks</u>	<u>barked</u>
<u>wave</u>	<u>waved</u>
<u>play</u>	<u>played</u>
<u>add</u>	<u>added</u>
<u>paint</u>	<u>painted</u>

Page 179

I <u>run</u> home from school every day.
Yesterday, I <u>ran</u> faster than I ever did.

I <u>swam</u> in the old pool every day last summer.
Now, I <u>swim</u> in a new pool near my house.

Last week, I <u>spoke</u> to the librarian about tarantulas.
Today, I <u>speak</u> to her about scorpions.

Now you <u>see</u> me jump over the fence.
I <u>saw</u> you do it many times.

Yesterday, we <u>took</u> our music books out into the school yard.
Today, we <u>take</u> our math books.

I <u>wore</u> Mom's hat yesterday.
I <u>wear</u> my own hat now.

ANSWERS

Page 180

I <u>am</u> good at many things.

He <u>is</u> good at many things.

She <u>is</u> good at many things.

They <u>are</u> good at many things.

I <u>am</u> thinking very hard.

They <u>are</u> going to Little League together.

I <u>was</u> going with them.

But they <u>were</u> leaving too early.

She <u>is</u> climbing the tree.

They <u>are</u> going to try to climb the tree.

I <u>was</u> trying to climb it yesterday.

Many kids <u>are</u> trying to climb the tree.

Page 181

I **visit** my Aunt Fatima all <u>the time</u>. Yesterday, Aunt Fatima ~~visited~~ a fortune-teller! Tomorrow, I (**will visit**) the fortune-teller, too.

Aunt Fatima **tells** me whatever she <u>thinks</u>. Yesterday, Aunt Fatima ~~told~~ me that the **fortune-teller** was magic! "She (**will tell**) you amazing things," Aunt Fatima said.

Dad and I ~~drove~~ to the fortune-teller's house. My dad **drives** pretty fast. Someday, I (**will drive**) a little slower.

I ~~was~~ a little <u>nervous</u> this morning. Dad says he **is** a little nervous now. But the fortune-teller (**will be**) very kind, Aunt Fatima promised.

I ~~saw~~ someone inside the fortune-teller's window! And I <u>see</u> Aunt Fatima's car parked outside! Could Aunt Fatima be the fortune-teller I (**will see**) today?

Page 182

Callie <u>eats</u> cereal with chocolate on it. Etsuko <u>enjoys</u> crab apples. Jake and Jim <u>were</u> at the store. They <u>bought</u> cereal, chocolate, and crab apples for their friends.

Shereena <u>is</u> a character in a tall tale. She <u>was</u> as tall as a big oak tree. She <u>made</u> her clothes out of tree trunks. She <u>jumped</u> so high people thought she <u>was</u> flying.

When my cousin <u>comes</u> to town, we all <u>hide</u>. His mother <u>says</u> he <u>is</u> a good boy. I <u>think</u> he <u>is</u> good only when he <u>sleeps</u>. My cousin <u>cuts</u> up strips of newspaper just for fun. Then he <u>eats</u> them! My cousin <u>is</u> a little bit strange.

Page 184

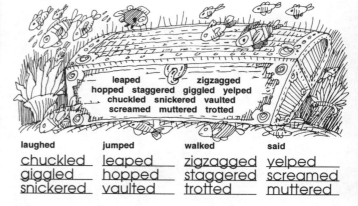

leaped — zigzagged
hopped staggered giggled yelped
chuckled snickered vaulted
screamed muttered trotted

laughed	jumped	walked	said
<u>chuckled</u>	<u>leaped</u>	<u>zigzagged</u>	<u>yelped</u>
<u>giggled</u>	<u>hopped</u>	<u>staggered</u>	<u>screamed</u>
<u>snickered</u>	<u>vaulted</u>	<u>trotted</u>	<u>muttered</u>

Page 185

Amy wore a <u>red</u> (sweater)

Christopher has on <u>big, old</u> (shoes)

Jessica wears <u>tiny, blue</u> (earrings)

Anthony wears a <u>huge</u> (jacket)

David clomps around in <u>heavy, brown</u> (boots)

That is Amanda's <u>beautiful, green</u> (umbrella)

I saw Daniel's <u>shiny, new</u> (sunglasses)

Maisie wears <u>unusual</u> (clothing)

Christopher likes his <u>squeaky</u> running (shoes)

Everyone likes to copy <u>clever, creative</u> (Maisie)

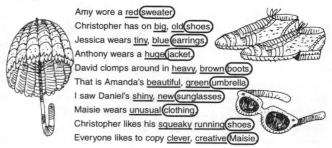

ANSWERS

Page 186

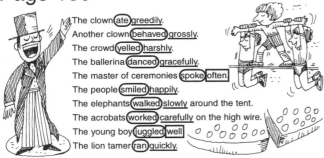

The clown (ate) greedily.
Another clown (behaved) grossly.
The crowd (yelled) harshly.
The ballerina (danced) gracefully.
The master of ceremonies (spoke) often
The people (smiled) happily.
The elephants (walked) slowly around the tent.
The acrobats (worked) carefully on the high wire.
The young boy (juggled) well
The lion tamer (ran) quickly.

Page 187

Everyone <u>knows</u> that a Cyclops is a round, ugly creature with
   one eye in the middle of his head. (**know, knows**)
It was getting dark when I first saw this <u>scary</u> monster. (**scary, scarily**)
He came <u>slowly</u> toward me. (**slow, slowly**)
He gurgled <u>horribly</u>. (**horrible, horribly**)
He had one huge <u>red</u> eye in the middle of his head. (**foot, red**)
I <u>circled</u> slowly around the Cyclops. (**circle, circled**)
I waved my long, skinny, <u>claw-like</u> fingers in the air. (**claw-like, claws**)
I <u>jumped</u> at the Cyclops. (**jump, jumped**)
The Cyclops leaped back <u>clumsily</u>. (**clumsy, clumsily**)
Then he walked away, shaking <u>his</u> head. (**their, his**)
When I saw his <u>sad</u> eyes, I was sorry. (**sad, sadly**)
But then the Cyclops shook his head at <u>me</u>. (**my, me**)
"I'll be back!" he roared <u>loudly</u>. (**loud, loudly**)
I hate to admit it, but I was about to run away as <u>quickly</u> as I
   could! (**quick, quickly**)
But then the Cyclops <u>disappeared</u>. (**disappearing, disappeared**)

Page 188

On special festivals, lots of knights <u>meet</u> to eat <u>meat</u> pies.
Sir Homonym was known as the <u>one</u> who <u>won</u> pie-eating contests.
At one festival, Sir Homonym <u>ate</u> <u>eight</u> whole pies.
Once, he saved my <u>aunt</u> from an attack of a man-eating <u>ant</u>.
She was <u>so</u> grateful that she decided to <u>sew</u> him a new shopping bag full of pies.
She would not pay one <u>cent</u> to have the bag <u>sent</u> through the mail.
My aunt walked <u>for</u> <u>four</u> miles and left the bag on Sir Homonym's doorstep.
The <u>knight</u> came home very late that <u>night</u>.
A <u>mist</u> covered the land, so he <u>missed</u> the pie bag laying on the doorstep.
When the <u>horse</u> tripped over the pie bag, the knight yelled in a <u>hoarse</u> voice.
You never heard a <u>grown</u> man <u>groan</u> like Sir Homonym did when he fell
   off the horse.
But when his <u>nose</u> smelled the pies, he cried, "Pies in a bag! Somebody
   <u>knows</u> what I like!"
"<u>Oh</u>, my!" he whispered after he took his first bite. "I must <u>owe</u> someone a big
   thank-you note for these."
<u>Right</u> away he sat down to <u>write</u> my aunt a very nice card.

Page 189

Draw lines to connect the words that are synonyms.

look — watch
like — enjoy
make — build
turn — twist
shake — shiver
find — locate
take — grab

little	teensy	sound	noise
part	piece	large	enormous
ill	sick	silly	funny
creepy	scary		

Page 190

on	off
start	finish
hot	cold
over	under
early	late
friend	enemy
lovely	disgusting
boring	dazzling

ANSWERS

Page 191

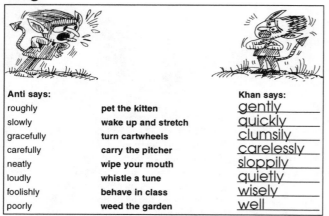

Anti says:

roughly	**pet the kitten**
slowly	**wake up and stretch**
gracefully	**turn cartwheels**
carefully	**carry the pitcher**
neatly	**wipe your mouth**
loudly	**whistle a tune**
foolishly	**behave in class**
poorly	**weed the garden**

Khan says:

gently
quickly
clumsily
carelessly
sloppily
quietly
wisely
well

Page 192

Josh sang ~~bad~~ **(badly)** because he had a cold.

Mandy walks ~~slow~~ **(slowly)** down the hall.

That **(boy's)** ~~boys~~ dog is very cute.

All the ~~boy's~~ **(boys')** jackets were left on the playground.

She lost just one **(tooth)** ~~teeth~~ this year.

Many ~~woman~~ **(women)** came to see the third grade show.

Kevin ~~wash~~ **(washed)** every dish in the sink.

Jack and Jill ~~give~~ **(gave)** their friend some stickers.

Jessie ~~brush~~ **(brushes)** her hair every morning.

Mac ~~wish~~ **(wishes)** he could get a new mitt for his birthday.

Sarah counted all the ~~pennys~~ **(pennies)** in her bank.

If you have ever **(seen)** ~~saw~~ a giraffe, you know they are big.

Freddy and Ginger **(seen)** ~~saw~~ their neighbors at the pool.

Sam ~~give~~ **(gave)** Michelle two books to the school book sale.

Justin spoke ~~quick~~ **(quickly)** because he was excited.

Page 193

Write a contraction from the list for each word phrase.

are not	aren't	can not	can't
did not	didn't	have not	haven't
would not	wouldn't	does not	doesn't

Draw a line connecting each word phrase with it's contraction.

it is   you're
she is   he's
he is   it's
who is   we're
they are   she's
you are   who's
we are   they're

Page 194

Some Things About Some Kids

Ferdinand <u>won't/doesn't/can't</u> whistle and spit at the same time.
Wee Willie Winkie <u>can't/won't/doesn't</u> go to bed on time.
The brothers Gerk and Geek say <u>they're</u> not really brothers.
They say they <u>aren't</u> even related.
Doorchester is always saying, "Knock, knock, <u>who's</u> there?"
My friend Halo and I always tell people that <u>we're</u> best friends.
The evil twins said they <u>weren't</u> even in the room when the
    fish tank fell.
My cat <u>won't/can't/doesn't</u> eat mice, because she's too refined
    and elegant.
People often would say I need a bath, but I <u>don't</u> agree.
Drusilla is the one <u>who's</u> standing on her head.
When someone says, "Why did you do that?" I always say,
    "I <u>haven't</u> a clue."

Page 195

an ape		a gorilla
a puppy		an orangutan
an elephant		a trunk
a soda		an ice cube
an egg		a creature
a game board		an abacus
an elf		a fairy
an umbrella		a raincoat
a sneaker		an illusion

306

ANSWERS

Page 197

Mr. **H**ank **S**nodgrass

King **S**waddlebottom

Dr. **S**ally **P**illaday

Judge **A**. **B**ythebook

Professor **T**homas **T**akeahike

Officer **P**utcherhandsup

Miss **L**ynn **F**orkitover

Queen **A**nn of **B**onjour, **F**rance

Good **E**ats **R**estaurant and **G**as

Slamdunk **C**ity, **T**exas

Boondoggle **E**lementary **S**chool

Emperor **H**inglesnaffer **W**hatchamacallit

Lotsalaughs **C**omedy **C**lub in **K**neeslapper, **I**owa

Page 198

Monday, **O**ctober 12: **S**am **H**ammenegg in **H**ouston, **T**exas

Saturday, **D**ecember 8: **D**r. **J**uan **S**tetoskopes in **A**capulco, **M**exico

Tuesday, **F**ebruary 23: **M**iss **Z**ha **Z**ha **V**avavoom in **P**aris, **F**rance

Wednesday, **M**ay 5: **S**ir **D**ingo **S**tark in **M**anchester, **E**ngland

Sunday, **J**uly 18: **M**s. **H**oagie **J**ean in **P**hiladelphia, **P**ennsylvania

Friday, **A**ugust 30: **M**r. **M**ehta **S**umit in **N**ew **D**elhi, **I**ndia

Thursday, **S**eptember 27: **T**ete **M**akesela in **M**orondava, **M**adagascar

Page 199

December 20, 2000
Dear Greg,
How's the water in Acapulco, Mexico?
Please call us at night on
December 31, 2000 so we can say
Happy New Year!
Love, Mom and Dad

May 10, 1999
Dear Greg,
We hope you are having fun
in Manchester, England.
We miss you. Is it raining there?
Love and kisses,
Mother and Dad

July 20, 1999
Happy birthday, Globetrotter!
We are mailing your presents
to Philadelphia, Pennsylvania.
Ring the Liberty Bell for us!
XOXOXOXO,
Mom and Pop

October 2, 1999
Dearest Greg,
We're so glad you're coming home
from Morondava, Madagascar!
You'd better hurry so we have time
to make a Halloween costume!
Lotsa love,
Mom and Dad

Page 200

In my backpack I have paper, pencils, money, and cards.
I like to travel in cars, trains, buses, and planes.
I sent cards to Sara, Patty, Kevin, and Jamal.

Page 201

Gemma is my best friend.
Who is the sentence about? Gemma

Gemma and Maisie are sisters.
Who is the sentence about? Gemma and Maisie

The dog with the big ears is cute.
What is the sentence about? The dog with the big ears

The beautiful ballet costume was white.
What is the sentence about? The beautiful ballet costume

My arms and hands are very strong.
What is the sentence about? My arms and hands

The subject of this sentence is **Annabelle Lee**.
Annabelle Lee lived by the sea.

The subject of this sentence is **the horse**.
The horse flicked its tail at Edgar.

The subject of this sentence is **the bell at the schoolhouse**.
The bell at the schoolhouse rang for three hours!

Page 202

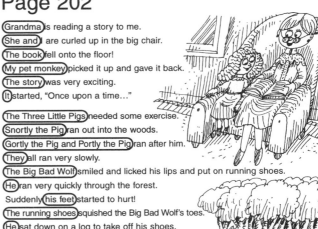

Grandma is reading a story to me.
She and I are curled up in the big chair.
The book fell onto the floor!
My pet monkey picked it up and gave it back.
The story was very exciting.
It started, "Once upon a time…"
The Three Little Pigs needed some exercise.
Snortly the Pig ran out into the woods.
Gortly the Pig and Portly the Pig ran after him.
They all ran very slowly.
The Big Bad Wolf smiled and licked his lips and put on running shoes.
He ran very quickly through the forest.
Suddenly his feet started to hurt!
The running shoes squished the Big Bad Wolf's toes.
He sat down on a log to take off his shoes.
Then he went home to soak his feet in the bathtub.
The Three Little Pigs got away—this time!

Page 203

Snortly, Gortly, and Portly are the three Pig brothers. The Big Bad Wolf is their neighbor. They are not the best of friends. The fence between their houses is 15 feet tall.

One day, the Pig brothers throw a party. All of the food is ready. The guests arrive on time. But when Portly turns on the music, nothing happens! Portly's stereo is broken!

Suddenly, Gortly hears some beautiful music. A lovely tune comes floating over the 15-foot fence. It must be coming from the Big Bad Wolf's house, he thinks! Together, Gortly, Snortly, and Portly tiptoe outside and peek around the fence. A piano is sitting right there in the yard! And the wolf is playing it.

ANSWERS

Page 204
Answers will vary.

Page 205

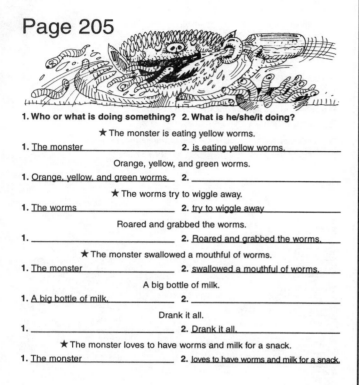

1. Who or what is doing something?   2. What is he/she/it doing?

★ The monster is eating yellow worms.
1. The monster   2. is eating yellow worms.

Orange, yellow, and green worms.
1. Orange, yellow, and green worms.   2. _____

★ The worms try to wiggle away.
1. The worms   2. try to wiggle away

Roared and grabbed the worms.
1. _____   2. Roared and grabbed the worms.

★ The monster swallowed a mouthful of worms.
1. The monster   2. swallowed a mouthful of worms.

A big bottle of milk.
1. A big bottle of milk.   2. _____

Drank it all.
1. _____   2. Drank it all.

★ The monster loves to have worms and milk for a snack.
1. The monster   2. loves to have worms and milk for a snack.

Page 206

statement Wendell painted his bike bright orange.
question Why did he do that?
statement Wendell lives in an apartment building.
X a different school
question Do you know Wendell?
statement Wendell is strange and I like him a lot.

Page 207

Someone was in the house.
Was someone in the house?
The dog has fleas.
Does the dog have fleas?
Your favorite music is rock and roll.
Is your favorite music rock and roll?
Jasper has green hair.
Does Jasper have green hair?
The plant will grow taller.
Will the plant grow taller?
Minnie can turn a cartwheel.
Can Minnie turn a cartwheel?

Page 209

Howdy! ★What's new, chickaboo? I've got a great idea. Why don't we all go jump in the mud? I love ★rainy days! There is nothing better than rain on your face and mud between your toes. Let's ★go! Why aren't you guys following me? First I'll roll up my pants. Yikes! This mud puddle is very deep. Oh, ★no! I'm in up to my waist. Will somebody please help me climb out? Yowza! ★That mud puddle was more than I bargained for.

Yuck !
Why don't you let anybody else talk ?
I think you have an awful lot to say .
Quiet already !
Gwendolina, where are your manners ?
What's a chickaboo ?
You're dripping mud on the floor !
Can you sing as well as you talk ?
Gross out !

Page 210

book   puppet   dog

man   nine

Page 211

gr	br	cl	fl
groan	bring	clap	fly
grumpy	brother	clatter	flashlight
dr	**fr**	**pl**	**str**
drip	french	playground	stripes
drive	fry	planet	string

ANSWERS

Page 212

th
thirteen
thud
thousand
thank

ch
check
cheese
choose
chick

sh
sheep
shop
shine
shape

Page 213

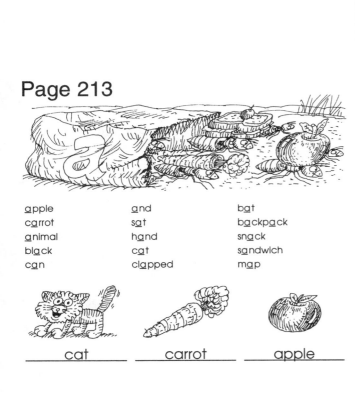

apple
carrot
animal
black
can

and
sat
hand
cat
clapped

bat
backpack
snack
sandwich
map

cat   carrot   apple

Page 214

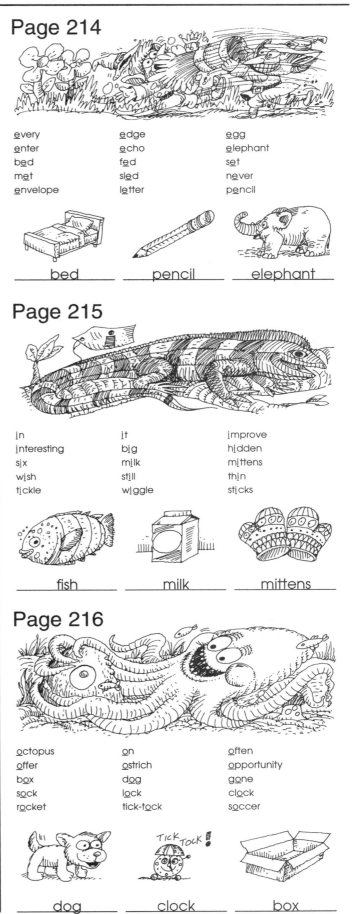

every
enter
bed
met
envelope

edge
echo
fed
sled
letter

egg
elephant
set
never
pencil

bed   pencil   elephant

Page 215

in
interesting
six
wish
tickle

it
big
milk
still
wiggle

improve
hidden
mittens
thin
sticks

fish   milk   mittens

Page 216

octopus
offer
box
sock
rocket

on
ostrich
dog
lock
tick-tock

often
opportunity
gone
clock
soccer

dog   clock   box

ANSWERS

Page 217

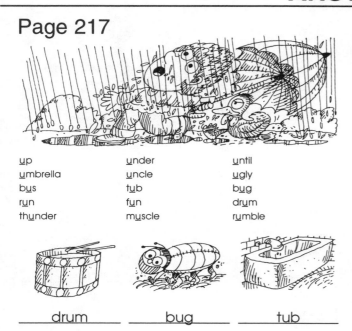

u̲p	u̲nder	u̲ntil
u̲mbrella	u̲ncle	u̲gly
bu̲s	tu̲b	bu̲g
ru̲n	fu̲n	dru̲m
thu̲nder	mu̲scle	ru̲mble

drum bug tub

Page 218

n̲e̲st rabbit

ch̲i̲ck p̲i̲cn̲i̲c ba̲sket

gra̲ss tru̲ck

du̲ck

jumping

pig dress

ru̲nning

dog fence

w̲i̲ndow

Page 219

hat (cake)	(tree) net	fish (bike)
(coat) frog	sun (mule)	(dime) six

skip	(game)	not	wet	(tune)
(slide)	sand	(note)	(beet)	fun

Page 220

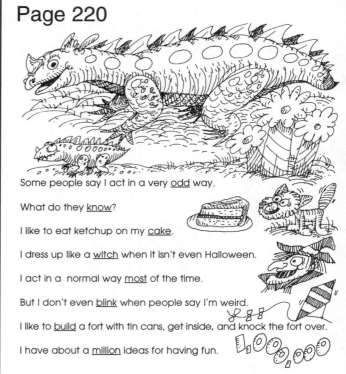

Some people say I act in a very <u>odd</u> way.

What do they <u>know</u>?

I like to eat ketchup on my <u>cake</u>.

I dress up like a <u>witch</u> when it isn't even Halloween.

I act in a normal way <u>most</u> of the time.

But I don't even <u>blink</u> when people say I'm weird.

I like to <u>build</u> a fort with tin cans, get inside, and knock the fort over.

I have about a <u>million</u> ideas for having fun.

ANSWERS

Page 222

Look in the word box below. Find a pair of rhyming words to complete each rhyme. Write the words in the blanks. Do the same on the next page, too!

When I can't do something, I moan and I <u>sigh</u>,
but I never or hardly ever really <u>cry</u>.

One day at the beach, I looked in my <u>pail</u>.
Swimming in there was a baby blue <u>whale</u>!

My teacher thinks I'm really <u>great</u>,
because my homework is never <u>late</u>.

I took some yarn and look what I <u>made</u>.
To clip to my head, a long yellow <u>braid</u>!

whale	braid	sigh	great
pail	made	cry	late

Page 223

wool	home	known	roll
full	comb	bone	bowl

My hair is a mess cause I just left my <u>home</u>
with a ball and a bat but not with my <u>comb</u>.

The pancakes you made tasted like <u>wool</u>,
but I'll tell you instead that I'm really <u>full</u>.

First I'll have some juice and a <u>roll</u>,
then cereal crackling in my <u>bowl</u>.

If only, if only, if only I'd <u>known</u>
you just got a dog! I'd have brought you a <u>bone</u>.

Page 224

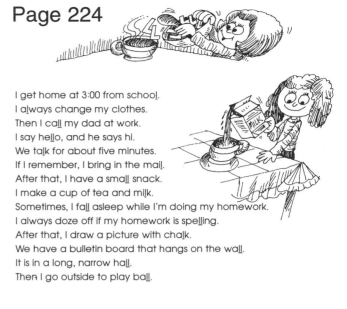

I get home at 3:00 from schoo<u>l</u>.
I a<u>l</u>ways change my clothes.
Then I ca<u>ll</u> my dad at work.
I say he<u>ll</u>o, and he says hi.
We ta<u>l</u>k for about five minutes.
If I remember, I bring in the mai<u>l</u>.
After that, I have a sma<u>ll</u> snack.
I make a cup of tea and mi<u>l</u>k.
Sometimes, I fa<u>ll</u> asleep while I'm doing my homework.
I always doze off if my homework is spe<u>ll</u>ing.
After that, I draw a picture with cha<u>l</u>k.
We have a bulletin board that hangs on the wa<u>ll</u>.
It is in a long, narrow ha<u>ll</u>.
Then I go outside to play ba<u>ll</u>.

Page 225

not becomes <u>note</u>
cub becomes <u>cube</u>
kit becomes <u>kite</u>
plan becomes <u>plane</u>
bit becomes <u>bite</u>

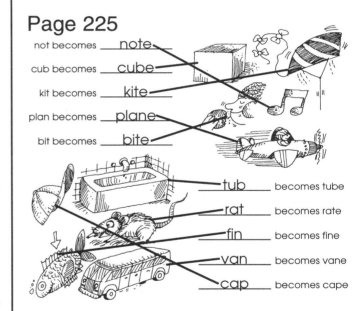

<u>tub</u> becomes tube
<u>rat</u> becomes rate
<u>fin</u> becomes fine
<u>van</u> becomes vane
<u>cap</u> becomes cape

ANSWERS

Page 226

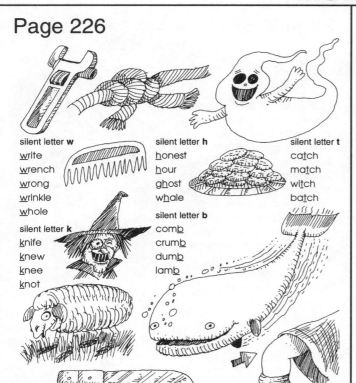

silent letter w
write
wrench
wrong
wrinkle
whole

silent letter k
knife
knew
knee
knot

silent letter h
honest
hour
ghost
whale

silent letter b
comb
crumb
dumb
lamb

silent letter t
catch
match
witch
batch

Page 227

I was sitting in my front yard talking on my cell <u>telephone</u>.
A huge, gray <u>elephant</u> came walking down the street.
I tried not to <u>laugh</u> or giggle when he said, "I've lost my circus."
"That's too bad," I said. "That's really <u>tough</u> luck."
Then he began to sneeze and <u>cough</u>.
"If you hold your breath long <u>enough</u>, you will stop sneezing," I said.
"To stop sneezing I usually say the <u>alphabet</u> backwards starting
    with Z," he said.
"You seem to know a lot about letters, vowels, and other <u>phonics</u>,"
    I said.
"Yes," he said. "My friend, the swimming <u>dolphin</u>, taught me."
"That sounds like one <u>fantastic</u> fish!" I exclaimed.
"Actually, a dolphin is not a <u>fish</u>," he corrected me.
"I like you," said the elephant. "If I promise not to play too <u>rough</u>,
    can I move in with you?"
"Why not?" I said. "I would like that very much. My mom likes me to
    have as much <u>fun</u> as possible."

Page 228

Page 229

comb + s = combs
camera cameras
note notes
crayon crayons
flower flowers
feather feathers
frog frogs
elephant elephants
orange oranges
rabbit rabbits
ladder ladders

horse horses
lion lions
chimpanzee chimpanzees
newspaper newspapers
onion onions
flute flutes
skateboard skateboards
peanut peanuts
sailboat sailboats
truck trucks

ANSWERS

Page 230

class	classs	(classes)	**peach**	peachs	(peaches)
beach	(beaches)	beachs	**dress**	(dresses)	dreses
fox	foxses	(foxes)	**match**	matchs	(matches)
kiss	kises	(kisses)	**fax**	(faxes)	faxs
ax	(axes)	axs	**mess**	messs	(messes)
brush	(brushes)	brushs			

Page 231

candy __candies__
puppy __puppies__
penny __pennies__
hanky __hankies__
sky __skies__
french fry __french fries__
butterfly __butterflies__
good try __good tries__
kitty __kitties__

Page 232

One	More Than One
woman	women
man	men
child	children
foot	feet
tooth	teeth
mouse	mice
goose	geese
leaf	leaves
hoof	hooves

Page 233

When I was a little girl, I <u>tasted</u> some delicious cookies. I <u>wiggled</u> and <u>moved</u> around while I ate them. Sadly, I <u>spilled</u> some milk on my dress. My mother <u>decided</u> we should wash the dress. We <u>entered</u> the laundry room. Then we <u>loaded</u> the washer. We <u>added</u> some laundry detergent. Then we <u>closed</u> the washer door. The machine <u>whined</u> when we <u>turned</u> it on. Mom and I <u>played</u> a game of hopscotch and <u>baked</u> some more cookies for a while. Then we put the clothes in the dryer. Soon, they were ready! We <u>folded</u> them up. Then we <u>shared</u> some more cookies and milk. The funny thing is, this time Mom <u>spilled</u> milk on herself!

Page 234

hug	**stir**	**clap**	**grab**
hugged	stirred	clapped	grabbed
plan	**brag**	**skip**	**trip**
planned	bragged	skipped	tripped
nap	**wrap**	**chat**	**bat**
napped	wrapped	chatted	batted
beg	**hop**	**stop**	**drop**
begged	hopped	stopped	dropped

Page 235

er
her
nervous
verb
serve
burger
nerd

ir
chirp
girl
sir
squirrel
third
skirt

ur
blur
burp
burger
curl
hurt
fur
purr

ear
learn
search
heard
earn
pearl

One word belongs in two different lists. Write it here! __burger__

Page 236

After the holiday party at <u>school</u>, I started to feel a little <u>sick</u>. Nothing major: just a belly <u>ache</u>. I try to look <u>cool</u>, so I took my <u>comb</u> out of my <u>pocket</u> to fix my hair before I said, "Dudes, I'm going to <u>make</u> my <u>escape</u>. It's time for me to see the <u>doctor</u>." (You see, my Mom is a doctor!) Then I grabbed my <u>backpack</u> and ran out the door.

I live just one <u>block</u> away, so I <u>walked</u> home. I opened the front door with my <u>key</u>. Soon, Mom was home from the <u>market</u>. "Hi, <u>cutie</u>," she said. She gave me a big <u>kiss</u>. Then she felt how hot my <u>skin</u> was, and listened to my <u>stomach</u>. Mom is so <u>kind</u>!

"I'll bet a <u>nickel</u> I know what the problem is," she said. "Too many <u>Christmas</u> cookies!"

ANSWERS

Page 237

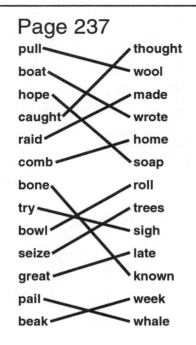

pull — wool
boat — home
hope — wrote
caught — made
raid — thought
comb — soap

bone — trees
try — roll
bowl — sigh
seize — late
great — known
pail — whale
beak — week

Page 239

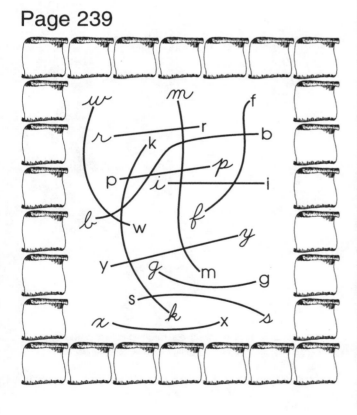

Page 241

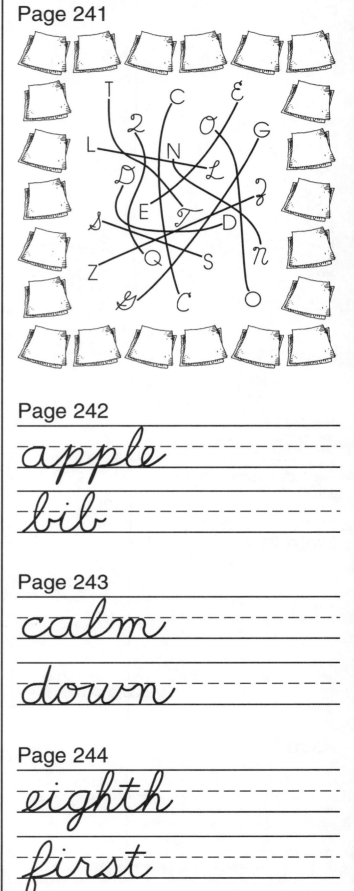

Page 242

apple

bib

Page 243

calm

down

Page 244

eighth

first

ANSWERS

Page 245

golly

help

Page 246

ice cream

jellybeans

Page 247

kitten

love

Page 248

milk

nice

Page 249

onions

pickles

Page 250

quarrel

run

Page 251

start

thunder

Page 252

up

vest

Page 253

wishes

xylophone

Page 254

yawn

zoo

ANSWERS

Page 255

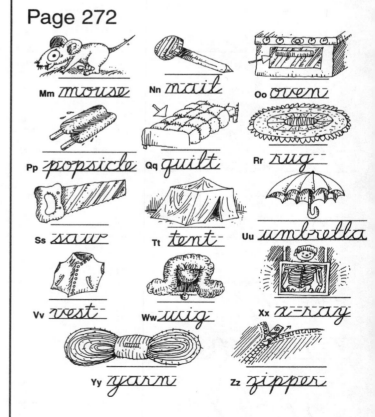

Page 267

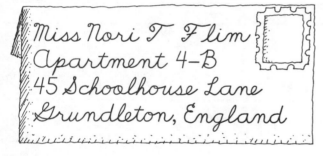

Miss Nori T Flim
Apartment 4-B
45 Schoolhouse Lane
Grundleton, England

Page 268
Answers will vary.

Page 269
Answers will vary.

Page 270
Answers will vary.

Page 271

Aa ant
Bb bird
Cc cat
Dd doll
Ee egg
Ff fish
Gg goat
Hh hat
Ii ice
Jj jewel
Kk key
Ll lemon

Page 272

Mm mouse
Nn nail
Oo oven
Pp popsicle
Qq quilt
Rr rug
Ss saw
Tt tent
Uu umbrella
Vv vest
Ww wig
Xx x-ray
Yy yarn
Zz zipper

ACHIEVEMENT CHECKLIST

Use the checklist below after each session with this book. If your child had trouble with a page, find the problem skill and list the page number in the middle column. You'll want to return to it later. If your child successfully completed the pages containing a skill, put a check mark in the "Mastered" column. Your child can watch with pride as the column fills up with skills he or she has mastered.

BASIC SKILLS	Needs Work	Mastered!
READING		
Following directions		
Reinforcing letter order		
Using context clues		
Sight reading		
Recalling details		
Identifying cause and effect		
Sequencing Finding the main idea		
Analogies		
Classifying		
Evaluating information		
MATH		
Using doubles		
Addition		
Subtraction		
Associative property		
Mental math		
Skip-counting		

BASIC SKILLS	Needs Work	Mastered!
Place value		
Rounding		
Addition with regrouping		
Subtraction with regrouping		
Estimating sums		
Multiplication		
Division		
Algebraic thinking		
Fractions		
Adding / Subtracting decimals		
Adding / Subtracting money		
Comparing money amounts		
Telling time		
Measuring		
Graphing		
LANGUAGE ARTS		
Nouns		
Verbs		
Synonyms		
Adjectives		
Adverbs		
Homonyms		
Antonyms		
Contractions		
Articles		

BASIC SKILLS	Needs Work	Mastered!
Using capital letters		
Using commas		
Identifying subjects		
Identifying predicates		
Sentences as complete thoughts		
Statements		
Questions		
Exclamations		
Using periods, question marks, and exclamation points		
SPELLING AND PHONICS		
Consonants		
Blends		
Digraphs		
Long vowels		
Irregular spellings		
Silent letters		
Alternate spellings of rhyming words		
Cursive writing: uppercase letters		
Cursive writing: lowercase letters		

Diploma

Awarded to

_____

- - - - - - - - - - - - -

_____

for extraordinary achievement in 3rd Grade Basic Skills

on this date,

_____

- - - - - - - - - - - - -

_____

CONGRATULATIONS!

Smart Kid